The
SORROWS
of
PRIAPUS

Consisting of
The Sorrows of Priapus
and
The Carnal Myth

For Harold Billings,
my dear, good friend

The
SORROWS
of
PRIAPUS

Consisting of
The Sorrows of Priapus
and
The Carnal Myth

EDWARD DAHLBERG

Harcourt Brace Jovanovich, Inc.
New York

ACKNOWLEDGEMENT

The author wishes to thank Mr. Paul Carroll, editor of *Big Table Books*, Coburn Britton, former publisher of Horizon Press, and now publisher and editor of *Prose*, and Mr. Warren Roberts, director of the National Foundation on the Arts and Humanities for their counsel and cooperation in preparation of this work.

INTRODUCTION

This is the age of cloacal nihilism; English is dead; we destroy our mother tongue, our sacred heritage, and call Caliban's brutal jargon the American language. A knot of scambling pedants will offer me flouts and fleers for saying this. But let it be; for I can sow dragon's teeth by saying anything at all.

I abhor the cult of originality, which is the creed of vulgarity. No Narcissus, I do not assume that I am my sole teacher. I go to the books of royal blood for my adages, roynish or sapid, I know not. And if I have been an orphaned Ruth gleaning stubble or a handful of grains in Boaz's field I never know whether some aphorism is the tares that has choked the grain.

Nor have I the stomach to hazard a single line without consulting Philemon Holland, Thomas Heywood's translation of Sallust's *Catiline*, Ben Jonson, Sir Thomas North, Robert Burton, Sir Thomas Browne, Robert Greene, Thomas Nash, or Isaac D'Israeli, the father of the English prime minister.

Also, like Swift, detest the plagiary; the cormorant criticaster who pilfers the works of others and alleges it is the consequence of his own pseudo-afflatus. As Pope stated: "And if he lies not, must at least betray." Or the critical bumbailiff who gets out a warrant of arrest for a book he cannot himself write. D'Israeli cuffs a reviewer of books, a "rhinoceros of a critic." Few among our false littérateurs have the conscience to calcine their spirit. I prefer a plain stupid man to the flaccid weather-vane intelligentsia in our bedlam society, or, as Jeremy Taylor puts it, "I shall entertain [them] in a charnel-house." Or send them to the vomitory.

Accustomed to being reviled, were I pusillanimous I would take what I had writ to house myself in it as a snail his carapace.

As for the prose style in *The Sorrows of Priapus*, if it is good it is an accident and the result of sidereal drudgery, and if bad I could find no favor with the Muse. I am not suggesting that the diligent labor of a writer is necessarily a touchstone of a gifted heart.

Could it be that *The Sorrows* is a calabash containing rose water, the olive of Minerva, the emulsion of almonds, and the marjoram that ancient Roman maids smeared on the gateposts of their paramours or fiancés?

Nor can I declare when an author should commence his work, or where: when the Pleiades set; or whether he drink hard water, close by a marsh, or near the briny sea; or in winter when the water is cold, muddy, mottled with snow and ice, and so most apt to engender phlegm. When I had a seizure of desolation I thought, or presumed, I wrote tolerably well; and on those occasions when I had brisk pacing days, nothing save bile flowed from my quill.

What then was my purpose in conceiving this erotical treatise. Ask a man why he was a grub instead of a kingly author when he made every effort to write a good book, and if he tells you he has a clear answer he is an underfoot liar.

When Socrates asked the cosmologists to explain their metaphysics they simply looked vacant; after he had made a similar request of the poet he combed his noddle. Likewise with Kant; when a pedant demanded that he elucidate the *Critique* he replied that he had something better to do than to suggest he had some swarming arcane exegesis in his intellect. Montesquieu was asked by dunderheads to explain why he philosophized, and he replied that it was simply to please the Venuses at court.

Commonly a man who tells you how truthful he is is a varlet. Maybe I am as "indifferent honest" as Hamlet; to be quite frank, I esteem a man who is not addicted to "the lechery of money," and without an addle brag displays by his deeds he is not a dissembler.

No prig, or cormorant, or flesh-monger, I consider it a windfall if some tender peat may be delighted with *The Sorrows*.

Let me assert I don't understand love; the dove is timorous but lascivious. That the romantic sensibility has gone clear out of the memory of the scatophagous novelist is a miserable dolor to our nation. Gargantua's Paedagogus, who is not fit to wipe the nose of his gulligut pupil, will call the

Sorrows insect lust, or a farrago of priapisms. What is clear is that I never sought to be a Master of Billingsgate or wrote for venal reasons. I abhor evil words and rabble writings.

Nor is *The Sorrows* supposed to be an aphrodisiac for lechers. It was a superstitious belief among ancient damsels and spouses that the mandrake would render them fertile; but, dear radiant Rachels, this plant belongs to the potato family. So, ladies and gentlemen, if you are still of the mind that the mandragora will provoke generation or increase virility eat mash and sausages. But know that the author of this phallic tractate venerates love. I cite as evidence divine Dante: "When we read how the desired smile was kissed by such a lover, he, who never from me shall be divided, on my mouth kisses me all trembling."

But to be altogether candid I sent this waif, *The Sorrows of Priapus*, into the world with fear. Did not Stendhal doubt his ability as a writer, and was not Corneille, who composed the *Cid*, looked upon by M. le Marquis de Danjeau as simply a "good fellow"?

One more word about ferine tropes and imbecile vernacular: they are the companions of low-born scribblers. When young women are slovens, and wear such short skirts as to well-nigh disclose their shameful parts, and men are attired in noisome drawers, literature evaporates, and the consequence is that America is being rapidly turned into a Doomsday country. John Ruskin speaks of the nobility of apparel; Plautus, the writer of comedies, mentions the sensuality of a delicate dame's garments. But when avaricious industrialists demand that brassières, panty hose, girdles be wantonly advertised on television, our national box of shame, our civilization is grounded upon impudicity.

Does this imply that trulls did not exist in other centuries? Indeed, that would be cant. Or that mayhap this is an apologia for *The Sorrows*? It is possible; for life embarrasses me, and I shame life.

During the reign of the French Valois the ladies at court were oftentimes loose, but they were deliciously covered, and though some were strumpets, many others engaged in amours that were not wormwood lechery. Boudoir wit and tender-hearted coition, good breeding and elegant prose stylists have vanished.

Do I meander? Anatole France claimed that the divagation is frequently more important than the theme.

However I may digress, the plight of authors has almost always been miserable. Should a writer resolve to be *un homme de lettres* he then takes the vow of poverty. In some respects, the writer is more alone—cloistered away in a rooming house—than in earlier times. Not always, of course. Memorable authors are isolated from one another, and one scribe is the whetstone of the higher faculties of another. Today, there's no Will's Coffee Shop or Mermaid Inn where Swift, Pope, Arbuthnot, Gay, Dryden, Addison, Steele can garner more understanding of literature from one another.

As for myself, I am garrulous as Democritus of Abdera; I'm a talkative animal. One can be loquacious and be a clod, another a sage. I can't even imply what I am. For who can weigh his spirit or his prate in Job's Balance?

I do avow that *The Sorrows* is now and then coltish, but it contains fables, maxims, nard, storax, and, I pray, a Peter's pence of thought. Nor is it void of herbs, flowers, plants, the erotical habits of beasts in the field or woods.

Books without waggery, and what the petit bourgeois prude would disdain, are a bore. Ask the camel why he won't drink clean water but must needs kick up a mere, lake, lagoon, or pond until it is muddy before he will swallow it.

Nor is *The Sorrows* cold or harsh. "Hardness of heart is a murderer"—Dekker. A boreal tract is likely to freeze the giddy hours and hopes the hearer requires lest he have nothing left except long bouts of melancholia, moroseness, and withal be in the dumps for weeks.

So there is, I trust, some salt in it; yet I quake lest this book be viciously misinterpreted or garbled by some hempseed who poses as a critical Rhadamanthus. One who makes a good poem or *Booke* runs upon the pikes. He is certain to be the prey of a toad-spotted judge of any littérateur whom he envies. Thomas Dekker affirmed: "For he that dares hazard a pressing to death (that is to say, to be a man in print), must make account that he shall stand (like the old Wethercock over Powles Steeple) to be beaten with all stormes."

Many suppose an author is the autocrat in our public weal, and that withal he has gained the affections of multifarious persons. Should he be fortunate he has one, two, or three steadfast friends; generally his adherents at first blush are his meek acolytes, but soon as they become overfamiliar they are shortly his turncoat companions and clandestine foes. Ford Madox Ford warned me to keep my distance from the mediocre book reviewer who laurels you privately and impugns you in the papers, whilst he gives fantastical encomium to draff that is sure to disappear in a brace of years and then to be interred for an eternity.

I have been abused of setting up a Prophet's Shop, and this by a hack of fustian who sent me epistles of genuflexion. What I see I sometimes by mistake foresee. No haruspex, I don't inspect the entrails of birds to prognosticate the future. Euripides held: "It behooves us, sacrificing to the Gods, to ask for good things, but to let alone prophecies."

Let him who scrawls dross civet his maggoty brain if he can, or take up some scullion trade.

Let us admit that life is bad luck; nobody except a gudgeon would be an author.

Of course, there were always jealous factions among authors; the renowned Ben Jonson lampooned Dekker (Crispinus in Jonson's *Poetaster*), but Dekker, no rustic witling himself, nettled Jonson in his own pasquil, Dekker's *Satiromastix*. William Hazlitt, another great man, was married to a frigid wife; he then fell into an absurd passion with a chit who was the daughter of a bawd who ran a lodging-house in London. Hazlitt exposed himself to the ridicule of a legion of enemies by plainly revealing that he brought this rapacious schemer sundry gifts for a few thin embraces and insipid Tartuffe kisses. Hazlitt's *Liber Amoris* was the laughingstock of these fell young blades, altogether calvish, and also the foes of John Keats. *Liber Amoris* is read unto this day, and those who viewed him as a toady of a daughter of a Mistress Overdone are in the cemetery of oblivion.

Dr. Johnson dismissed *Gulliver's Travels*, and maligned Swift as a penny father to his guests. Anyone familiar with Swift's immortal epistles will see that Swift abhorred parsimony. Who knows what clandestine motive Johnson had in assailing Dean Swift. No bottlehead, he had as much spleen as anybody else. None should fail to study Dr. Johnson's *Lives of the Poets*, spite of many obtuse critical errors.

An ignoramus on the West Coast considered me affectedly archaic because I employed such a simple word as *cully*, alleging it has not been in use since the earliest part of the seventeenth century. Evidently he was unfamiliar with Swift's *The Tale of a Tub* or *The Battle of the Books*.

Who is to decide what words are obsolete? Nietzsche opined that one had to depend upon "the conscience of the ear." Is there more ganglion in new-fangled neologies and fetid tropes that are up to date than in English derived from the sages of Letters?

Some remarks are pertinent regarding the purposes of an author. He does not embalm his manuscript in a sarcophagus; in the private drawer of his desk a book of regal worth so hidden can bring only a tear dry as a sherd for the writer. One who pretends he does not desire recognition for honorable work is a pettifogging quibbler. It is told that Sophocles expired with joy after he had received a prize for one of his plays, and that Aeschylus, informed that one who scrawled a mungrel poem had been rewarded for it, was so disconsolate that he went into voluntary exile.

Our memorable scribes of the nineteenth century either were ignored (Emily Dickinson and Herman Melville) or were mendicants (Henry David Thoreau and Edgar Allan Poe). Even unto this day there are beggars similar to those indigent outcasts in England who smeared spearwort on their faces to produce artificial sores, expecting that their condition would so wound a benevolent passer-by or a woodcock that he would receive from him a tuppenny. Others were content with the orts left in a trencher by a gorbellied squire.

It is my wish to chronicle a few of the predicaments of the writer. Myself, I have no cause to be peevish, for I have been panegyrized by many book reviewers who leaf the pages of a book they esteem with aspen pulses and immaculate probity.

I have no inclination to scribble a beef-witted, desiccated Introduction feigning to be the dragoman of the oracular reader. How I conceived *The Sorrows of Priapus* is beyond my ken. And it would be asinine to explain a book I have not even read for three lustra. Moreover, I haven't the stomach to go through *The Sorrows* in order to re-examine my foibles, a fatuous metaphor here and there or an indigestible simile. I suppose if an author knew beforehand what he was writing he would never have inked the volume. Therefore I decline to offer unknown hearers or reviewers what the Jews call a Midrash, an exegesis of Holy Scriptures, or, in this instance, a pompous elucidation of Priapus. Rather, I would be the unthrift, if I can, and attempt to do what is impossible to compass, that is, to sweep out the dunghill fiction from our American Augean stable.

I may add one example culled from Suetonius merely to show that man is a paradoxical brute, courteous, insolent, covetous, sycophantic, and an assassin. But I don't care a rush about the malice of the academic lotus-eater.

Allow me to cite one example in *Priapus*. It is impossible for me to despise Julius Caesar; more, I admire him; he had an astounding mind and was a writer from whom one can learn a great deal. True, he looted countries for his lemans; he may have given a foreign kingdom to provide cosmetics for Eunoe, wife of the Moorish king of Mauretania, whom he adored; he fell into a becrazed passion with Servilia, sister of Cato, his adamant enemy; and he sent his cohorts to cast ordure upon the head of Cato, senator and stoic.

Yet he often forgave his adversaries; when Pompey, his rival, whom he defeated in battle, escaped, he was discovered by a pair of rhetors, who slew him. Doubtless they expected to be well guerdoned for their crime. They were: Caesar had both of them decapitated. When the marmoreal poet Catullus lampooned Julius Caesar as a pathic, the Roman emperor invited him to his table; Caesar grew so fond of this immortal versifier that whenever Catullus's father invited him to lodge at his villa Caesar humbly accepted.

A sparse drinker of wine, he also had an indifferent palate. Another host asked him to come to his home for meat and salad; the former was rancid and the olive oil dreggy, yet, not to offend, he fell to it as though it were the most exquisite hors d'oeuvre.

Caesar destroyed the Roman republic, but who wants to dwell in a dour Catonian commonwealth? Every land was his purse, but name one man who is not in one way or another depraved.

It is held by Suetonius that Brutus was the issue of Servilia and Caesar, for their liaison was a long one, and Brutus was conceived about the time that Caesar first lay with Servilia. I can only defame the putative son as a parricide for caballing to murder Julius Caesar. "Man is sometimes good and sometimes bad," says Euripides.

Now I should return to the beginnings of *The Sorrows of Priapus* and *The Carnal Myth*, originally one volume.

James Laughlin, a penny-father, did not know how to induce people to lick the pages of such a manuscript. First, he thought of bringing out a fifty-dollar limited edition of *The Sorrows*, which he ultimately did. Before arriving at this crucial decision he had another idea: seduce the reader by offering him a book filled with illustrations, and then anticipate that after viewing the museum drawings, the onlooker would inevitably read the book! How many people who attend symphony concerts or go to a hundred galleries are devotees of literature? May I find no fault with Laughlin for his just intentions. In his own way, he was as much of a simpleton as I. Whilst I say this, may I also append to it that a writer may be a sage on the printed page but a fool all the days of his life.

Laughlin had to find a well-known artist, and he asked Ben Shahn to make forty drawings for a truncated *Sorrows*. So he asked me to select a moiety of the manuscript, which I did. He purchased very expensive paper for the limited edition in France and ordinary pages for the indigent student and reader. He then gave the manuscript to Ben Shahn, who after going through it said it was full of lickerish conceits. Finally he consented to do it, and for a very meager amount of money. Meanwhile, he had sent me a waspish letter accusing me of inditing a libertine book. I replied in kind, saying, "Who is Ben Shahn and what cause had he either to be born or to inhabit this pustular globe?" To his credit he was so taken with my reply that when the *Edward Dahlberg Reader* was published Shahn asked Laughlin to include my letter in that volume.

Sometime in 1967 I took what was later to be named *The Carnal Myth* (Truman Talley's title) to Horizon Press. The advance was so niggardly that I resolved to call on Victor Weybright, whom I earlier had met and liked very much. At Weybright's office he asked to see the manuscript, but I refused. "Look," I said to Mr. Victor Weybright, "if I take the manuscript away from Horizon Press Coburn Britton and Ben Raeburn will be so irked with me that should you decline it I won't have any publisher at all." And so I added: "Mr. Weybright, you can't see one line of it; take it or leave it," and he chivalrously accepted it, and gave me a handsome advance. *The Carnal Myth* was then brought out by Weybright and Talley in 1968.

Make no doubt of it, no matter how honorable a writer is he has to be a wily Iago with a publisher. Then in need of lucre, I met William Jovanovich, who was seated at one table whilst I was at another having luncheon with Victor, and Jovanovich came over, to shake hands with me, and to congratulate me for my autobiography, *Because J Was Flesh*.

Out of pocket, I telephoned William Jovanovich and asked for an appointment, and we lunched together at the recherché Brussels, and I asked him to be my publisher. I told him I was becoming as much of a lunatic as Gogol, who ran from one book house to another, and with a satchel filled with rejection slips. William Jovanovich jotted down on a card an advance he would give me for a book not yet finished. Still needy, I asked my sovereign publisher and friend William Jovanovich if he would not print *The Sorrows of Priapus* and *The Carnal Myth*. He considered it for a few seconds (he knows as well as I that delay is the disease of the soul, and in my case Rabelais's "flux of the purse"). He promised to combine the two books, really one, as I have said, into one volume entitled *The Sorrows of Priapus: Part One and Part Two*. When an artist came with his briefcase glutted with his paintings to Alfred Stieglitz at An American Place, and asked him to hang his canvases, Alfred Stieglitz crisply rejoined: "Are you willing to starve?" and when the suppliant declined, he (Stieglitz, who never took one penny as a commission from any sale of a painting by any of his artists) sent him away.

Generally I receive a letter weekly from a young prentice who wishes to be a writer, and although I invariably reply, and with civility, I say: "Do you want to go to the almshouse, and don't you realize there is no crueler occupation than that of authorship?" A memorable book should be a benison to America, but the writer either is eschewed or receives a very occasional grant which is not enough for him to keep alive so that he can complete a book. Lucian says that before Ulysses finished his exploits his name was NOBODY, and there is not one author in the U.S.A. who can predict his portion. Heine said he asked for bread and was given a headstone. So, dear, gentle reader, don't epitaph me, READ ME. SELAH!

PART I

The Sorrows of Priapus

This is a fable and not natural history. The polestar of the writer is a legendary book, using geography, the beasts in the earth and in the sea, and voyages, as the source of maxims, mirth and an American myth. To accomplish this many narratives have been employed; in two instances I have done little more than paraphrase Athenaeus and Aristotle's *Animals* which I also regard as a remarkable fable though both Buffon and Humboldt held the Stagirite in the highest esteem. Plato, St. Augustine, Clemens of Alexandria, Pausanias, Hakluyt, Diego de Landa, Sahagun, Pigafetta, and innumerable other mythographers and discoverers have been my inward seas, tides and life. This is a book for brave readers and poets.

Edward Dahlberg

PROLOGUE

SING Venus Hetaera; Priam had fifty wives, and Darius went to battle with three hundred and fifty concubines; sing Venus the Courtesan who has sunk the Theban towers. Aspasia sacked all Hellas, and Gnathaena pillaged the pockets of the poet Diphilus.

List the courtesans as Homer catalogues the ships at windy Ilium: Chrysis, Corone, Ischas, and Antycra, who quelled many Argives, and relieved Pericles, Aristotle, Aristippus and Sophocles; let them be recollected, and savored once more, and thrice again as an ox's chine.

There were Telesis, Dippthese, and her whoring mother, and Theolyte who grew rotten hands and hunkers at her

3

trade; the dearest thighs of virgins came from Ithya and Hellade. At Abydos, one of the four great towns of fishy Hellespont, there was a temple of Venus the Prostitute. When Solon saw it was impossible to bridle the youths of Athens he imported tarts from Corinth and Megara, and employed some of the revenue which the women earned to erect a statue to Venus the Strumpet. Aspasia and her college for whores are as necessary to Athens as abstemious Socrates.

Pious Greeks bring cakes and sesamum and the orchites of stags and wolves to chaste Artemis the Huntress who rules Ephesus where every year they hold a Whore's Festival called Aphrodisia. Lacedaemon has given us Cottina whose name is a rumor of pleasure throughout the Levant, and she is immortal, for a brothel bore her dear name. Give homage to Phryne, for in her heyday, when she gathered capers, she was worth the thirty keels Nestor commanded at Troy.

At the rising of the Dogstar the swordfish go mad for the female; boars propagate their species with joy; vipers take a long time when they are intertwined. Consider the snows of the Alps; Eudoxus and Euclid winter all lechery; the intellect is a hot plague, loud with boasts. The cephali have large heads; cuttlefish have as much ink as Euripides; skin is slime and sand. Men at first, says Empedokles, were eels, graylings, polypi, seathrushes.

Avoid cucumbers, gourds, violets, watercress, and the soft blows and amatory kicks from the Marathonian women. Boiled torpedo done in oil and wine is indigestible and inflammatory; one bed and one wife is philosophy; age withers all wives; the sea-cuckoo has a dry rump which lames the tribe of fish; 'tis best. Copulation is a dangerous pastime.

Darius promised any man who invented a new pleasure a

4

large reward. Cotys, King of Thrace, prepared a marriage feast for Artemis, and waited for hours for her to come to his bed. The sole testament and bequest of the physician Nicostratus was a huge quantity of hellebore which he left to his whore. The great Stagirite named his ethics after his son Nichomachus who was the issue of a harlot. Ptolemy Philadelphus lay with Didyma, Billisticha, Agathoclea, and Stratonica, for whom he built many monuments along the seashore. Clito, Alexander's cupbearer, wore only the lightest tunic, and held in her right hand a cornucopia, which is a sign of seminal wealth. Many splendid houses in the ancient world bore the names Myrtium, Mnesis, Pothina, although Mnesis was a flute player and Myrtium a notorious doxy. Agathoclea was Ptolemy Philopator's prostitute; she ruled him who was supposed to govern Egypt, and ruined both. Hieronymus, the tyrant, fell in love with a common bitch he met in a house of ill-fame, and he made her queen of Syracuse. The king of Pergamus was the offspring of a flute player. Ptolemy, one of the Hundred Companions, was the issue of a whore by Alexander's father Philip.

Greek worship was a theology of bawds. The statues of Demeter, the hymns to Persephatta, and the paintings of Daphne were a scholium on venery. Alcman invented the first songs of lust, and Nicander, the poet, called the goddess of amours Aphrodite Kalligluttus, the strumpet with the marvelous rump. Praxiteles thought the bitch of love resembled the figure of his mistress, Cratine, and all the painters, who paid visits to Phryne to copy those parts which send men to Tartarus or to the almshouse, were patrons of the *muliebria*.

The nereids, nymphs, hamadryads, naiads came out of the sporting houses of Elysium. Aphrodite, the lover of virilia, sprang from the scum of the sea; others say from the gore from the genitals of Uranus. The masculine gods were whoremongers; Hephaestus, the humpback brazier, as licentious as a fuller, tailor, weaver, potter, was miserable until he married Aphrodite who forsook him for Mars. There was Zeus the Ant, so named because he assumed the shape of that insect in order to have intercourse with Eurymedusa. Jove could never empty his testicles; he lay with Europa, and threw the orchites of a ram upon the breasts of Demeter because he had raped her. Every watery image aroused Poseidon, who deflowered Amphitrite, Anymone, Alope, Alcyone, Hippothoe, Chione, who are sea foam, breakers, tidal waves. The titans were insatiable; Hercules gathered fifty maidenheads in one night. He had at least fifty offspring and was not regarded as exceptional in copulation.

The rituals of these gods and goddesses are mystical sexual bouts. Semiramis, another title for Astarte or Ashtoreth, slew every man after she had enjoyed him. The Athenian women celebrated the rape of Persephone, which they called the mysteries of Thesmophoria; the frenzied women at this ceremony carried the sacred chest of Bacchus which contained his prepuce. They baked sesame cakes, pyramidal cookies, and brought lumps of salt which were emblems of Priapus. In the orgies of Cybele the drums were beat, there was the sounding of cymbals, and the fig branches that were held aloft resembled the phalloi. The comb, marjoram, and lamp of Themis represented her secret parts.

Beauty is the tomb of the race of men who crave ruin. There was no wanton running after women when Numa and King Tullus Hostilius ruled, for justice and the character of woman were held in higher regard than her navel or licentious toes, though the Sabine maids were most appealing.

"Beauty is . . . a short-lived tyranny," remarked Socrates. Theophrastus called it a silent deceit. Each person has a deity in him which is ravaged by a frump.

Socrates said that nobody ought to be in the company of beautiful persons. Gorgias, the Leontine, lived eighty years, and said that the reason he had all his faculties was that he never did anything solely for pleasure. Before the average man reaches fifty his intellect is a senile carcass. Men of talent lose their minds earlier, for they compose their iambics for money to bring to Venus. Archytas of Tarentum said that no more deadly plague than the pleasure of the body was inflicted on men by nature. Lycon, the peripatetic, came to Athens for an education, and he learned first of all what each streetwalker costs.

The mind is as easily thrown down as the senses. The Greeks said Eros was the son of Isis and Zephyrus, which proves that erotical love bends under the softest wind. Aristophanes informs us that Eros goes as far back as Chaos; Plato in the *Symposium* asserts that Eros has no father or mother.

Pleasure is intractable, and it is told that Semiramis, called the wild pigeon, was the first one to castrate women, because people are mad for what is new or dangerous. Men spend their lives swallowing anchovies, polypi, onions and plebeian carrots, which either make them diuretic, or give them the potencies of pigeons, who are said to require the longest time in their hymeneals.

Man used to wipe his hands on the crumbs of bread and he was safe. Adam passed water and thought nothing of it. He defecated in a clump of leaves and had no lawless sensations. Now voiding is ecstatic and every one perishes for the stroke of a hand or a foot. One should wive an unsociable she-dragon, or a sloven who won't sit, or stand up, or lean, or lie down, for everything raises up a host of profligate longings.

A man may have the testicles of a newt, or wear the rugose coat of a she-frog to be repulsive, or persecute his gullet and abdomen to kill all desires until he weighs no more than one obol, but he is likely to be inflamed, attract a dowd, or have enough concupiscent skin to want a tittle more.

No matter how we long for virtue who wants to be a spado? Even the bull, just after he has been castrated, mounts the heifer once more showing that habit masters nature for at least one copulation. Nor should we give credit to the cold; Alexander never touched the daughters of Darius, because he had little inclination for women. Olympias, his mother, gave him the Thessalian courtesan, Callixene, hoping to cure him of his indifference toward woman, as she thought him to be quite impotent. After the sack of Troy each monarch returns home with a concubine, except Menelaus, who had wasted his genital powers in Asiatic orgies and so required none.

Why does this sadden the abstemious? Does it really matter whether a man can raise his pudendum or not? We are gluttons, greedy, inconstant, and wild asses, for no other cause than this ludicrous exercise. A legendary swan lives three hundred years, and a goose to be eighty, and though some only live long enough to be a goose, the longevity of the former would not diminish lust. What would the multitude do with a longer life except ask for a longer gullet or penis? All the feasts for Persephone, Daphne, Cybele, and the frantic, mystic shouting of *Hevoi*, which is the pagan Eve, or fornication, is nothing else but begging useless idols to give us the ability to rear up this ugly tyrant at the sight of any chit, girdle, or cestus. Since all is lost what harm can

8

there be in a quick perusal of the whore's register of renowned Hellene?

There were Neaera and Phila who wore out her teeth in service, and Nais who had none; and Anticyra who only drank with crazy men. Glycera was the universal friend, and Nanium cheated her customers, for she was astonishing in her garments, but without them showed a listless navel and a brace of turnip legs. Phryne, who razed every husband to the ground, and put to the fire and sword his household, bore herself in public like a sibyl, only disrobing for the whole of Greece on the feast of Posidinia. Had she not observed all the holy days of Venus, that jealous goddess would have slain her, because there was no flesh under the moon to glut men like Phryne's. It is told that Lais of Corinth, who had kindled the fury of that deity, was beaten to death by a footstool in the fane of Aphrodite.

Olympia assuaged the rotten fever of Bion, the Philosopher; Theoris served Sophocles in his old age; Homer gives Phoenix as a mistress to the aged Nestor; Archippa, the heiress of his plays, lay with Sophocles when he was skull and wrinkles. Once when her former lover was asked where Archippa was, he replied, "Why, like the owls, she is sitting on the tombs."

Nicarete satisfied the bed of Stephanus the orator, and Metanira coupled with Lysias the Sophist, and both these courtesans were enemies of all mankind, one solacing an orator and the other a sophist. Philyra, Scione, Hippaphesia, Theocles, Ismathe, Lagisca, and Anthea forsook their occupations, after which time husbands became greater adulterers, going to other men's wives instead of harlots, and stealing out of windows in bags of chaff. This larded deceit, falsehood and cant, for nothing good ever comes of the virtue of a whore. Herodotus praises Naucratis for its beautiful wenches; it is said that Stilpon the philosopher had as his pupil Nicarete of Megara, but she should have confined her metaphysic to his sheets and pillows. Billisticha came from the house of Atreus, and her favors were dear. Leme could be had for two drachmas, and her name means the matter that gathers in the corners of the eyes, a poor name to be purchased for money.

But here is the wind in the paunch of Falstaff, and some filberts for Caliban. Consider the operations of the testicles; will you be Solon or tread a thousand whores and live to die senile? What is copulation that man should be tickled into dotage? Are we born solely because the red mullet and the sea perch have wombs? Shall we eat honey and locusts, or be Agrippina?

I

MAN must be classed among the brutes, for he is still a very awkward and salacious biped. What shape he will assume in the future is vague. There are many traits of early man he has lost, and it is plain that he is much more given to falsehood, robbery and lawsuits than the primitive. The first two-legged man scratched himself because he had an itch. Men now lie and steal for this pleasure. Primeval natures wallowed without thought, but soon as men began thinking how pleasant it was to rub themselves and to have deliriums from mud, they employed their minds to achieve what paleolithic mankind did without being lascivious.

Men lie, not alone for profit, but to root in Circe's mire. No pigmy or cave-dweller wears more bizarre or dirty raiment than present-day man. He is often as offensive as the gland on the back of the Brazil peccary. He would rather tell a lie than the truth because his sole purpose is to be a grub.

He is the most ridiculous beast on the earth, and the reason for this is his mind and his pudendum. He sacks nations, or throws away his reason to see the petticoat of Aspasia or Helen empurpled by murex or the lichen at Madeira. The procreative organ in the camel is behind, but in man it is in front, and unless he is too fat to look over his belly, he pays more attention to this gibbous organ than to his arms, his talus, or anything else. He frequently forgets how his arms look, and is surprised to find a wen on his jaw, and he rarely knows whether his pupils are brown or ochreous, but he is always mindful of his testes hanging between his legs like folly.

In the *Book of Enoch* the scribe says that the first two-legged creatures had the private parts of great studs, and it may well be that Methuselah and Jared and Mahalalel were mountains and that from their middle hung hills which were their organs of generation. Otherwise, it is impossible for one to imagine how they could live for nine hundred years without wearing out their genitals. It is known that Og, King of Bashan, had an iron bedstead seven cubits long, and that the giants of Anak had six fingers.

Adam bare stones long before he begat Seth. Human life began as procreative mud, and later man was a shark with a human face. There was a human species with a lion's mouth and the legs of a giraffe, for anterior to the neolithic period diverse animals mingled. Many of our traits are found in the countenance of the bear and in the lip of the pard. The story that the pigmies were chased from the River Strymon by cranes is also a fable of our bird origin.

The old gods were ocean, rivers, animals, fish, birds; Noah was a fish, and Plato supposed that Oceanus was the father of Saturn, and there is as much natural history in this as mythology. Men and rivers are demigods and beasts; the Scamander is the river's mortal name; Zeus called the fierce water Xanthus; in the *Iliad* it is reported that the bird, said to be named *chalcis* by the gods, was Cymindis among men. This is the heroic conception of human fate.

Pleasure brings about the most violent transport in men, and of all the animals in the earth none is so brutish as man when he seeks the delirium of coition. Democritus of Abdera, unable to bear being stung by any female foot in sandals, or round skirt, was said to have plucked out his eyes. He was as mad as a boar for the shape of Venus; when the testicles of the boar are swollen he is at times so beside himself that he rubs them against a tree until he is castrated. The female deer hates copulation because the penis of the stag is as tough and spinous as a palm leaf; the pain the stag gives her is considerable but she cannot overcome her passion for him.

* * * * *

One marvels what man will do to have his skin scraped. Antony lay with Cleopatra at Daphne for this foolishness, and though he gave all his force to her, his delights were not as long as those of the ordinary fly. One cannot submit a little to sexual excitement without hankering after more such raptures. When birds are continent their testes are internal, but after sexual intercourse the penis is very conspicuous.

Whether man is more lecherous than the partridge is doubtful, but he is not as chaste as the raven, who bleeds from the eyes during coition. The man of sensibility is not satisfied with ordinary coupling; all the arts of Lais of Corinth cannot furnish his skin and veins with the infinite sen-

13

sations he demands. Pain affords him infatuate happiness unknown to four-legged creatures. He is almost the only animal that cohabits at all times. With the exception of the pigeon, a bird which abstains only a few days in the year, man has the most lickerish tail of all beasts. This has made him very unruly, and double in his words and deeds. Unlike the elephant he has no seasons for his venery. This pachyderm, after impregnating the female, avoids this excitement for two years.

The elephant is an exemplary teacher. It is in many respects a rational animal, and repents of its anger, which is rare among men; when it kills its master, it grieves and sometimes starves to death. The dam suckles her young six years, and many elephants live as long as people. When an elephant is sick he is given wine to drink, and when he has an eye disease, these warm, friendly orbs are bathed in cow's milk. His wounds are healed by butter. These are the simples that the Homeric heroes gave to each other at Troy, and the poet of the *Iliad,* as well as Plato, would have paid the tenderest regard to this superior beast whose diet, medicines and habits are far better than those of the vast multitudes in the earth. The elephant, doubtless, was no less a monitor than the heifer which is so often seen beside the seated Buddha.

Countless adulteries are committed without lust, and with no thought to the peril which attends this folly. Animals do not give each other the pox; when men attempt to lie with a beast it rejects the malady that is said to be the companion of human genius. The adulterer is more senseless than the earthworm who keeps part of his tail in the hole he inhabits when copulating so he can disappear at once should he see an adversary. The tibulæ hide in the hedges all day, and seek the delights of the female at dusk.

14

Most people are furtive, but very few are ashamed; the elephant prefers to copulate near an obscure river bank, and the camel retires to the desert to rut. Modesty has been undermined because it is not generally known that the camel, more continent in his thoughts than a modern vestal, requires a whole day to complete such exercises.

Few labor for anything else but to exchange their sexual properties with blowsy dowds, or to rival the fox which has a bony penis: even the impotent are like the aged boar who waits for the tired female to lie down before he will risk his feeble appendage.

When the camel opens its mouth it looks like the greatest ass, though the ancients made the strongest bowstrings out of its pudendum. The egg of the *sepia* pretends to be black myrtle seeds; the vine the polypus deposits is its ovum.

The rhyades remain quiet until the equinox, and the grasshopper is said to sit upon the olive and reeds when it casts its skin, but man now stays in one place only long enough to void or feed. His irregular habits and haste make him the inferior of the polypi which unite only in winter, and these creatures conceal themselves for this reason for two months.

The tortoise gives a month to coition. The moose cannot have commerce with a red deer that is too short, but men and women of sundry sizes are suitable to each other. Andromache had too long a body, but not for Hector. Nubian dwarfs were ravishing morsels in Egypt. The pigmies who rode on the backs of partridges, which was a way of saying they were concupiscent, satisfied the giantesses of the Thermodon.

The puma never utters a cry when he mingles with the female. Bucks and does herd separately after the rutting season; man is incontinent whenever he has the occasion.

Men are more obscure to themselves than the elm or marine shells. The *solens* perish after they have been taken away from their borning place; the fir is comely in the sun, and the cedar is a Saul in the mountains. Man does not know when he should plant, or from whom he can glean, or what town is his stony Medusa. The *sepia* deposit their ova near the river Thermodon, for its waters are warm and potable; the eels seek reedy ponds, and the pregnant red mullet lies among the rockweed. Paul the Fourth was an ascetic until his eightieth year, but when he became pope, he sported for hours at table as any mare in heat.

Men are too unstable to be just; they are crabbed because they have not passed water at the usual time, or testy because they have not been stroked or praised. The habits of animals can be ascertained better than the mien of a philosopher. When stags are bitten by the *phalangius* they eat crabs and are healed, but if a man has had a poor or dour sleep, he is waspish the whole day, and is likely to curse his parents.

There are certain fish that only breed in the Pontus, and many of the tunnies run to the Pillars to spawn. The *halcyon* appears only at the setting of the Pleiades and during the solstice. The crocodile is a modest brute whose penis and testicles are internal, and he could be regarded the peer of saints did he keep these members there. The polypus hides its ova in holes which is a lesson for modern women who, when they are with child, go through the streets showing the results of their shame. When the mare wants to sport with the stallion she makes water. But this lubricous mammal is continent compared with man, and he eats herbs, barley and oats which is a diet similar to the sacred table of Pythagoras. One has to travel to India to find a savant as herbivorous and savory as this extraordinary brute.

We scoff at Alexander for burying his horse Bucephalus,

but the stone of that stallion shows that he had the separate toes of a human being, and this monument stands in front of the temple of Venus Genetrix. Bucephalus was so named because of the breadth of its head. Plato means wide forehead, and it is interesting to add that the philosopher came of the family of Hippias who were horsemen. The horse is so marvelous to behold that Semiramis was seized with the wildest passions when looking upon this carnal beast.

The horse goes mad pasturing by himself; separated from the human flock man loses his reason. Nietzsche, the wildest intellect of his century, lived in solitude, a Dionysiac disease which in crazy horses was known as the hippomania. In his last Bacchic throes he flung his insane arms about a horse standing in the gutters of Turin.

No one but a perverse person takes exception to horse manure. Droppings of many animals are more healthful than those of people. Human dung, except that of primitive races, is unclean. When the stag's horns are most perfect he has a very offensive odor; unlike man, who wears the same skin all his life, the stag casts his horns, the bird moults, and the despised python sloughs off his vile coat; man's despair is that he smells; he is garbed in the same skin until he rots in the tomb.

The Aztecs sold pots of human excrement for working their leather. Civilized nations regarded primitive man as a savory beast. The ancients, having the highest esteem for the offal of kine, said the oxen of the Sun were stalled near the Ocean where the sea scum resembled dung.

Man imagines that because he stands on his legs he is intellectual, but the penguin is a biped who feeds until he can scarcely move; the bear too can stand up. Man's passion for disorder, upheaval and bedlam explains his greed. He attempts to prove that whatever man does is for his advantage. This is not true of him, and sometimes quadrupeds, generally reasonable, are demented or perverse. It is fabled that the mongoose breaks the eggs which the crocodile hatches in the mud though it does not eat them nor derive profit from this act. Man's neck is as long as Plutus: Solomon said, his eyes cannot be filled with seeing nor his ears with hearing. He is so bored that he seeks the naive existence of the sow. Having devoured all the experiences possible to the biped, he now wants to be primitive which he thinks is the same as being chaotic, torpid, or supine the whole day. Baudelaire asserted that he had the wildest desire to be aboriginal, because standing on two legs was too trivial and average for him. Man imagines that could he crawl again as an infant or as any brute in the field, he could recapture a primeval existence. Others are only content with the testicles of animals. Could man moult his skin as the bird its feathers, and have new flesh, he would be innocent. The stag casts his horns every year, and the horse may lose his hoof, but each acquires what he has shed. When the teeth or the hair of men decay, they do not grow the tusks they show whenever they desire sexual frenzies, or the hair that makes them prance and sport and neigh. Were it possible for man to shed his feet or his hands he could have a naive heart.

Man pines to live but cannot endure the days of his life. The learned, crouched over their inkpots, covet the customs of the savage who cohabits with a Lais or Aspasia of the Amazons whenever he pleases, or envy the panther. The poet wants to be an animal. "Submit, my heart, sleep the sleep of the brute," said Charles Baudelaire.

Men have more sorrow from their entrails than animals; except backward people or ancient races they have fewer rites pertaining to their ordure. They excrete when they are bored or want a savage pleasure. The father of Beatrice Cenci drew the close-stool over to the fireplace and voided in the presence of his wife and daughter.

The Mohammedan of the old order wipes his buttocks with his left hand since he uses the right one to handle food, plant vines, or to greet people. A Moslem woman can divorce a man with a reeking breath, a fault unknown among the natives of Otaheite. Modern man rushes to the water closet, and after the most summary ablutions, extends his hand to the first person he meets. The ancient Essenes had strict tenets regarding defecation and its burial in secret places. Man at present dungs in his own house and considers himself a delicate creature.

The anthropoid is arrogant, and when he finds a remedy for a malady that is the consequence of a cormorant throat he is elated. Tantalus can never eat or drink enough countries, rivers, or carcasses, and this gluttony is the cause of nearly all human woes.

When the sow has a certain disease, it goes to the mulberry for relief, and when the horse falls into a declining melancholy, the sound of the flute will assuage this fever for which men have found no nostrum. The river horse, after overeating, comes ashore and presses its hide against the sharp rushes until blood flows from a vein in the leg. When ill the stork sups upon marjoram; and stags also, in failing health, graze upon wild artichoke. The pigeon has exquisite revulsions, and at times disrelishes his table as much as men, and then turns to bay leaves for food.

Despite all the spital houses in the world, if a man suffers from strangury, can he do much more than the Sudanese who entreat their idols to let them urinate without difficulty?

If it please Zeus may we pass water; to prevent chafing, if Cato be true, put a small branch of Pontic wormwood under the anus.

* * * * *

Socrates described love as the sting of a tarantula. We see that desire dominates the old as well as youth; the senile forget to button their clothes, and leave the door of their trousers ajar, showing what is no more than a relic of a quondam tower. Men lose their goatish powers long before their minds; Montaigne complained that when he was somewhere in his fifties he could not raise that sleepy animal more than three times a week.

The anthropoid is more luckless and unintelligent than animals, and the remedy for his ills is not progress, going forward, which is always to his grave, but turning backwards. He has extirpated most of the beasts which he no longer has as tutors. As a result he does not know whether to cohabit with woman, with man, or with sheep, and there are some who are enormously aroused by the sight of a mare. There is a breed of dog that will copulate with a wolf, and it is believed that a species of dog is derived from the tiger, and there is the Babylonian cameleopard; but, for the most part, the stallion seeks the female of its kind, and the elephant hankers after the same sort of animal that bore him.

Man is more incoherent than any beast in the earth. Schopenhauer has said that pleasure is the absence of pain, but it is not true. Man is not content with negative delights or even with positive transports. Some of his immoral deeds lacerate him, and he finds much satisfaction in being wounded. Man hates what he does, and that is what is moral in him, but he continues to do it, which is why he is Euripides, a spider, or the *Dryophis fulgida*. Man lies in ambush for all creatures,

20

for he is the hunter; the Psalmist cries out that he is the turtledove about to be devoured by the multitude.

The whelp is most greedy for the soul that has fallen down to the ground. In the *Psalms* the soul flees to a hiding place in the mountains. The prophet rides upon a Cherub who is one of the fowls of the air. Man who is the master of the sheep and the oxen has the tender feet of the hind. He crouches before the bulls of Bashan and dreads man continually. But a little while he is a tree planted by the rivers of water, for all lurk in lairs to harm his branches.

Man is either too stupid or vain to know himself, and too self-loving to understand anyone. He cannot endure his own vices in others, and he is least just when is railing at the faults of people.

Man is the tragic brute because he can never be as sure of others as the ass or the bull who knows that he is the booty of the wolf. A strong foe is better than a weak friend; the heron is always on guard against the eagle; the *anthus* is a reliable opponent of the horse since both covet the pasture. The deer when it has produced the fawn hides, for she knows what beast will hurt it. The wolf is the enemy of the ass, bull and fox; a mountain cat will embowel a porcupine; in a narrow defile the panther will leap upon a small dog instead of a human being. Men have no such certainties, and the more erudite they are the fewer companions they have. Aristotle in his old age said, "O my friends there is no friend."

Everything in man is double because he has testes. The old Nile god had the form of a man with a woman's breast wearing a cluster of water plants. The Egyptians extracted from the meanest worm the paint to design jars and the sacred, funeral amphoræ. In the time of the Pharaohs dense thickets were said to be the resort of malefactors. This was a proverb, and yet among the Quiché Mayans the gods were seated in the ravines, the forests and among the mosses. Not everyone that goes into the wilderness is Elijah or John.

If one considers the acts of his youth he wonders why he was ever young; or if he ponders his later vices he asks himself why he is still alive. In what manner is Messalina superior to the puma, or is anyone any better than a beetle which takes such pleasure in the fungus, called the English phallus, which has a most odious smell. The testicles of the American lizard give off a musky odor, and the monkeys in Brazil when stroked have as pleasant a scent as Alexander of Macedon. Priam had fifty bedchambers, and despite such opulent amorous experiences, had no more sense than to select as his consort the termagant Hecuba. Solomon's bed linen was fragrant with Sheba and the perspiration of a hundred concubines, but were they any dearer to the nostrils than the musky testes of the lizard? There is a paradox: the Egyptians claimed that their land was infested with scorpions until it was settled by Apis. The serpent in Eden gave Eve knowledge of the phallus, and this is the source of art, science, poetry, wisdom, and perfidy.

We weep because the human race is no better than it is. The aquatic frog has the tail of a fish until he makes a twig or a blade of grass his house, then he loses his tail and grows legs. Nature advises the frog far better than man; a noddle endeavors to employ faculties he does not possess, and the eunuch burns for Jezebel.

Where is Apollo who rested his foot on the skull of an ox; where are the wild horses, the fawn, the roe, the cubs of bears that were brought to the altars of Artemis? Shall we wed, or woo, or tremble?

II

IT IS OBVIOUS that we must imitate the habits of many quadrupeds if we are to be gentler.

The animal is still crudely limned, and this is also true of viviparous man. Though he is the one mammal that thinks, the embalmers at Abydos passed his brain through the nostrils. He is much more inconstant than animals. The eyes of the goat and the stag are of one color, and only in men are those two unstable pools of various hues.

He is altogether a double nature, having two lips, two eyes, a pair of feet, and a right and left hand. Man is a congenital hypocrite because he asserts that his purpose is simple. Should he aspire to be apodal, at least, he would have no feet to hasten him to evil.

The pouch between his legs is divided into two, but it can never be asserted that one testicle is the adversary of the other, but the two have one sole purpose. No one then dare be a disciple of a hedonist for the simple reason that it is hard enough to accomplish any idea or good work so long as people have two limbs, two crooked lips and double eyes which devour whatever the mind considers a benefit to others and a deeper nourishment of one's own nature. It is better to try to be continent and to fail than to be an epicure. Antisthenes, the pupil of Socrates, said that when he had any sexual needs he took whatever there was at hand, a trull, a slut, a vendor of vegetables in the Agora, and that she was exceedingly grateful.

Man is double, and who may know his heart: he is a moral hermaphrodite. When Zeus was asleep he dropped his seed on the earth from which grew a demon with the genital organs of a man and a woman. The gods cut off the male organs of generation of this androgynous fury, which produced an almond tree. After the daughter of the river Sangarious ate the fruit of the almond she conceived and bore a son who was suckled by a he-goat. Concupiscence and force are the source of all our actions, Pascal wrote. We eat the almonds and conceive, and all our sons are reared by goats.

Most people are satisfied in shoals, their noon is night and shame, and their dreams are the garbage of their days; man fetches his dreams with the same fetid food he baits the purpuræ. All his members are arrogant; the hands, the feet are terrible tyrants.

Man is born wanton, wild, and asinine; he succumbs either to good fortune or to evil tidings, being the toady of both, because he does not know what to do with his head or fingers, or what his mind or hands can do well. The loon uses his sharp head to pierce the water, and his broad, palmated feet as oars. The *New Testament* is the gospel of the hands, and few can comprehend the homely adage about the tares and the wheat because they have not the manual intellects of the lowliest publican or carpenter in Bethlehem. The muleteer desires to be Virgil, and the goat licks the olive of Minerva which was said to render it sterile.

The human hand, though it is divided like the foot of the panther, can write, and tenderly touch a child or a mother. The hand, still a residual talon, and when meanly made more predatory than the claw of an eagle, is a marvel to behold. Ezekiel's four Cherubim have an ox in one cheek and an eagle in the other, and though they are feathered, they have human hands. Unloving hands are avaricious horns; unable to caress they are too puerile and deformed for morals or sensual delights.

The Coaita is a large Amazonian monkey; unlike human beings he confines his sojourn, dwelling in the valleys and uplands of the Amazons. His prehensile tail is as close to a human hand as the New World has produced among the higher forms of mammals. Hands in America are strong and cunning, but loveless.

It is abominable to have the same hands and feet throughout one's life, because there is so much vice and shame in the old hands. What cupidity there is in each finger, and in what unclean places have they been, and how often they skulk or hide in pockets because they are parsimonious or debauched. Men with women's hands are often preferred, but long, narrow fingers and nails are more suitable for malign ends than for affection.

Sometimes, the hands of men are the parables of the body. No lion, pard, pelican or heron has the head of Euripides, or

Paracelsus, and one may surmise what a god was the occiput of Amos who was a gatherer of the Sycamore Fruits. The loins of the Angels are of burnished brass or of fire, and men when they are not hirsute are not entirely base. The ears of Aphrodite are small, rotund and toothsome, but the lobes of the male are a wallet into which he stuffs his greed, gossip, and carnal stupidity. Ears, often no better than the sow's, have a sluttish aspect; they root on the sides of the head, and like the pig can be fed mire and almost any filth.

The ears are worse than the navel because they cannot be hid. There are two kinds of ears, one which is a scale of justice in which all human pains are weighed, and there is the voluptuous ear which is a flute or a lyre, and which is always trembling; every man can play upon it, and receive some tune for his effort. One with fluted ears has eyes for wonders and marvels, and he is able to watch a poor man swallow stones and regard it more as a prodigy than a cause for pity.

The foot is far less wise and good than the hands or ears, and the toes are not so savory in aspect as the horse's hoof. Often human arms and feet are no better than the feet and fins of the cephalopod, and the mouth of the unintelligent is the tubular siphon of a squid. It is said that man alone has a face, though if one goes abroad this statement is likely to be denied.

The dolichocephalic head is wonderful to behold, and one can have some certainties regarding the cranium of a great faculty. It is easier, however, to recognize the head of a pompion or a gross churl than to discern a wise head. Homer informs us that the head of Thersites is peaked at the top; Thersites employs scurrile words, and is always reviling Odysseus, or Agamemnon, or Achilles for no other reason than that they are superior to him in understanding.

There is no greater ruse than the human physiognomy; the eyes, the nose, and the hands are subtle snares, and the most practiced observer is not sure whether the genius of the person is in the general expression of the entire character, or whether it is to be viewed in the behavior of the neck, or the shape of the nose. He who relies on the testimony of his eyes is very likely to be duped. The character of a person is as much of a riddle as the substance of the soul or the Intelligence of the Universe. In the Cherubim of Ezekiel the ox in one cheek is the ruminative side of the face, and the eagle in the other signifies power. Frequently one sees only the predatory eagle, for men employ their force for booty rather than as angels.

There are countenances which at first blush look like wisdom, but upon closer acquaintance turn out to be vacant. This is particularly true of the large proboscis on the face. Most men of considerable intellectual strength have a conspicuous nose resembling a potato, a squill, a testiculate cucumber, for the nose is the second phallus in the male. Besides that, it is the messenger to the testes, for virile olfactories not only take much delight in the *Analects* of Socrates or in the *Dialogues* of Plato, but they also revel in good weather, inhale the seas and fruits, and are very quick to capture the fragrant skin of Nicarete of Megara or the adulterous uterus of Clytemnestra.

Agamemnon had a heavy rather than a strong nose, and he was a coarse rustic soldier with women, for warriors are not acute in amorous matters, and for this reason was of little worth to Clytemnestra.

The small nose is regarded as more comely in a man, and though it is handsome in a face at table, it generally goes with a short, miserable penis in bed. Lascivious women run after men who have a nose the length of the small finger, but are grievously disappointed when they cohabit with them.

Although the elephant uses its nostrils as a hand, it cannot be said that an animal has a nose, which is the sign of a higher creature. The nose is not entirely intellectual, and though it is better formed than the testes, it is a residual privy organ, and in the prehistoric age men very likely used their noses for erotical labors. Today the nose is more inclined to scent the female than the *Nichomachean Ethics*. As Aristotle remarks, it is good to take pleasure in the smell of apples, but it is intemperate to dote on unguents and incense.

Next comes the mouth which when open is as gawkish as the blowhole of a fish. So long as man has a tongue he cannot be likened to the feathered tribe or with the majority of mammals. What ascetic can compare with the grasshopper which has no mouth and lives on dew?

Man is the animal that talks, but the Cosmos is an Act, not a word. Thoth is the alphabet god, and he is the first month of the old Nile year when the funeral papyrus was placed in the hollow wooden figures of Osiris, between the legs of the deceased. Since words have fallen into disrepute we will either return to glyphs or to the simple neighing of the river horse.

The tongue is even less covered than the scrotum, and can hardly ever be called a secret part since few men have enough character to keep it in their mouths. It is difficult to know whether the tongue or the phallus is more harmful to men. The panther and the lion remain in their lair far longer than the tongue will stay in the mouth. This member is the foe to the whole of mankind. Hermes has empowered it with speech, and its utterances are sometimes oracles. Still, there is no galled tail so hurtful as this organ. It is a thorn, a stone, and also a witling, for when it is not a thong, it is a fool, and man spends the greater portion of his life reprehending himself because he could not be silent. If he has nothing to say, he speaks it, and sometimes this adder stings and poisons a friend, without cause and, particularly, to express ingratitude to one who has been kind or bestowed upon him a benefit. Even when it is hid in either jowl, it is a sly animal. Everyone is its prey, and as it is said in the *Book of Esdras*, "The stroke of the tongue breaketh the bones."

There is no other part of the body that is so busy; the secret parts in the middle are often lame, but the tongue is rarely dormant, or lying content in its cave except when it has made a huge boast, or has encountered another asp that can wound more, is quicker in guile, or in unjustly assorting words together. Silent people are more prudent than the garrulous, and, though their tongues think rather than speak, they are untrustworthy. As man is not very intelligent it takes him a long while to recognize either his foe or his patron, and he often praises the man who is preparing his ruin, and has an insolent face for one who would give him prodigal affections.

Litigations, courts, legal documents and countless laws have been spawned by the tongue. The tongue of the fish is thorny, but not free, and the sacred Nile crocodile has no tongue, though it devours men, but it is still a more enlightened creature than human beings, because men eat men, and have tongues. The bird is said to be able to put its tongue out as far as the width of four fingers, and that is a very dispiriting fact. The reason that the tongue is hidden in the mouth is that it can hardly be proud of its vile labors.

Far worse than the human nose, often well-made, and the tongue, are the testes, the most ugly and ill-shaped member.

The phallus is a slovenly bag created without intellect or ontological purpose or design, and as long as the human being has this hanging worm appended to his middle, which is no good for anything except passing urine and getting a few, miserable irritations, for which he forsakes his mother, his father, and his friends, he will never comprehend the Cosmos. The *balagrus* are without ova or semen, but the Cherubim on the walls of the temple of Solomon were painted copulating.

The tail has grown weaker in apes and men. This is the fifth hand of both; it does as little climbing for some of the Cebides as it does for Pale Face. The scarlet-faced monkey inhabits the forest, and though it is never known to descend its short tail is no sign of terrestrial habits. Man, the fifth-handed climber, is weak; he is not among the branches, or on the ground, and where are the apples and olives of all flesh?

The phallus has always been considered an unkempt beast. Though matrons and virgins brought fillets and hyacinths to this rude, homely god, it was never his face, but rather his abilities that were worshipped. Ptolemy Philadelphus had a priapic image made that was one hundred and twenty-five cubits in length, and the effigy of this lewd brute was carried in the festivals either to Isis or to Osiris. Nearly every ancient idol was priapic. This was the god that protected the garden and seed-time, and who was associated with the melon, the leeks, the mandrake, and the apples of Haran which were aphrodisiacs. The onion was supposed to inflate the courage of the weak and the nervous. Hercules, the patron of the stoic, because he purged the Augean stables, and extirpated the robber Cacus, was at first commended because of his astonishing prowess in bed. This is not too likely. Giants are clumsy with Venus. One can hardly conceive of six-fingered Anaks as having amative wisdom. In neither the *Odyssey*, nor in the fragment of Euripides does Cyclops have any progeny. No women are seen in the monster's cave or island.

Man-eaters, giants, or the well-favored males have less skill with Aphrodite than gnomes or ugly men. Ovid asserts that cripples perform best. The Pythagoreans called lettuce the eunuch of the vegetables, and Adonis hid beneath a head of lettuce. Narcissus is an enervated lover; he is too vain to care for anybody, and so self-loving that he is not likely to have an erection, for nature will not allow anybody to get that excited about himself. He goes to a woman to have two admirers and not for other indecencies. Narcissus, or his semitic forebear, Ham, has no shame, and the wisest and best men in the world are those who are ashamed. The conscience of Saint Augustine and Tolstoi came from their shameful parts.

Meanwhile, since man is not going to be different for a thousand millenniums he should select certain animals to teach him to be just, eat and gender at regular intervals, and blush. A learned nature never ceases to be revolted by his privy parts which remind him of his nose and his tongue, that second illicit organ of the human being.

When people have been lawless for a half a century, they cannot master themselves at all. Plato may say that the pentagram is a symbol of the good, but all Euclidean shapes and abstractions and Pythagorean diet are no more than the avoidance of the troublous testes. Besides this, what is known as the creative organ is droll and as foolish as the visage of a mule, or a thumb, or a navel, could they smile.

The prepuce is a fatuous appendage, and the entire tribe of

pudenda and scroti have the heads of pigmies and the wrinkles of stupidity, decrepitude and mirth. This race, for the penis, despite the fact that it is attached to each person, has its own disposition; it goes where it will, and though the spurious owner wants to think, it wants to urinate, and if its helpless landlord desires to read or to sow grass, it wants to lie in bed; since it is only given to us as a loan or is leased to each one, man has little control over it. A man may want to study Mark, or Paracelsus, or go on an errand to do a kindness to an aged woman, but this tyrant wants to discharge itself either because the etesian gales are acerb or a wench has just stooped over to gather her laundry. The whole matter, when one thinks of it reasonably, is bizarre. The head is so obtuse as to go absolutely crazy over a pair of hunkers, which is no more than a chine of beef. Of course, the whole of human appetite is ridiculous, and although we are delighted to hear that after Ajax has returned from a furious battle with Hector, and has been lucky not to have been killed, Agamemnon gives him a leg of an ox as a reward. Naturally, Ajax is a very stupid man, but who is any better?

There is nothing more outlandish than the necessities of the scrotum and the anus. Lewd men are almost always eccentric; Charlemagne kept the prepuce of Jesus in a box at Chartres. Though good men often abhor their lascivious desires, the wether is also likely to be obscene; spados stood at the side of Phoenician Jezebel, who was a votary of Priapus; however, a eunuch came to the aid of the Prophet Jeremiah. Nothing can be foreseen because all men are unstable.

The saint cannot endure his skin; he is overthrown by his sense of smell, and pleasure lows in his ears all day. He is the prisoner of the least sound or touch; during the season of

32

coition the male fish is in such a state of excitement that if the female strikes his abdomen with her mouth he has an orgasm. The voice of the locust is produced by rubbing himself with his legs. What an odious thought for the seminal male. Origen yearned to be a fish or an apodal animal which has no testicles; but eunuchs burn and fish have young.

We are residual beasts, and though the Cosmos inspires the deepest awe and prayer in mortals, this satyr between the legs is the crudest in shape, and the Creator could not have given serious thought in its making. The Ocean is our father, and the Earth our mother, but the penis is an afterthought.

The will is the deity in man, but it sows its seed in stony places; Philo has remarked that where gold and silver grow naturally, grass and fruit do not. When the will dwindles, the spirit stinks. By soft rivers and willows men lament and love, and small waters produce legends; capes, streams, and promontories take their names from Venus, Adonis, and Sarpedon, for whom Zeus wept; but Aspasia and Helen putrefy. After summer has left her cheeks can Paris or Menelaus understand why Ilium was burnt? The Ethiopic soldiers revolted against their king because he scorned their valor. Quitting family and homeland because fate nourishes the heroic faculties more than the household hearth, they rang their spears against their shields, and lifting their garments above their genitals, said that so long as they possessed such weapons they could secure a new country and other wives.

III

RIOT, QUIET, AND SURFEIT are the consequence of sexual madness. Ten boars can easily tread a hundred sows, but this knowledge inflames the mind instead of pacifying the flagitious imaginations of men. The criminal joys of human beings are unknown to birds. There is no counterpart of Tiberius or of lascivious Messalina in the feathered races.

The great eagle has an iris of amber, and in appearance he is as vitreous as the topaz; this favorite of Jupiter was as regal and predatory as Heliogabalus, and the only difference between the bird and the emperor of Zeus is that the former will never touch carrion. The two Agrippinas, mothers of Nero and Caligula, were said to have had unnatural births, coming out of the womb feet first.

We go to the manners of birds, insects, quadrupeds, reptiles to comprehend mortals. Birds only couple in one way which has seldom been the ration of man. Ford Madox Ford, now among the woeful shades, rejoiced because swifts copulate on the wing. Every savant is a lewd goat or a sparrow of Venus.

Birds are reasonable creatures, and once we know whether they are insectivorous, nestle on trees, and how they copulate, their habits are as rigid as the laws of Numa. Numa Pompilius, Livy thought, was a wise legislator because he was an austere Sabine by birth and disposition, and not owing to any knowledge of Pythagorean discipline. Even predacious birds govern themselves in accordance with the laws of their nature, which they seldom transgress. Thucydides said that when the Median guests were slain by the Greeks, the ravens flew out of Peloponnesus; the carrion crow, the raven, the thievish jackdaw are great lawgivers. Man, whether he is violent, or peaceable, is lawless.

The pheasant sleeps on trees to avoid the foxes; the partridge, dreading the attack of the polecat and stoat, avoids coverts. Man is either too obscure to himself, or he skulks in coppices and hedges to conceal his motives, which are not entirely reasonable, because his grandfather was a descendant of insolent mountaineers, or his mother came from the loins of Lot.

The duck is a constant social animal; he arrives after his vernal flight when the swamps thaw. The age of the young eider is the calendar of the Greenlander. The Indian hunting season was called the goose moon because this was the time when wild flocks of these species made their regular appearance.

Wagtails follow the plough which turns up the worms to nourish them; nose flies swarm in the nostrils of horses where they lay their eggs; but the rational human biped is hoodwinked every day of his life, and he is a more arrant misologist than he who has little or forlorn hope of ever being reasonable at any time with anybody.

The meat of wild duck and geese has the flavor of the bog; primitive morals too are as rank and plain as the forest or swamp. Savages are neither the artists of Eros, nor poets.

The bones of people are related to their morals, but who can know the rapacious. The feathers clothe the legs of the eagle as far as the pounces, but the talons of men are hidden. The raven weighs ten to twelve ounces, and is most cunning, but can he compare in dimension and bulk with man? The percnopterus is a degenerate bird, but unlike the debauchee it has no agreeable traits to hide his character. White ernes ravage fawns, pigs and lambs; the fishy smell of the osprey discloses its booty. The osprey lives among the reeds, and the white erne builds its nest in the maple, the cypress, and in the pines; the solitary bald eagle nestles on the cliffs. Men live everywhere, marry anybody, and their prey are their friends.

Man is the most inconstant of companions. The pelican quits the river Strymon to incubate near the Ister; wild geese prefer icy Greenland. Each year the swallow goes to the aits on the Thames, and this regular habit is a proverb for the reed shaken in the wind. The widgeon takes her young on her back and flies to the marsh to avoid her foe the raven. Men scarce know how to scent an enemy or a friend. They smell pleasure rather than what is good, and like birds of prey have a cere which helps them to find their food. With this nostril of rapine man snuffs up the sophist, an iambic, the paintings of Zeuxis, the statuary of Polyclitus. He sees and hears as though he was always smelling rather than thinking. A just person, a kind nature, does not quicken this predatory cere. The odor of a good act, charity, friendship is much harder for the fowler to detect.

The scent in men is for hunting and selling; and a friend, as Socrates observed, is not to be caught as the hare is tracked. We must consult the gods, says the sage of Attica, to see whether they recommend a man as a friend. What incantations can we use or what sort of love potions concoct to charm a man into friendship? Socrates declared that he had friends who could not bear to leave him either day or night, and among these were Plato, Antisthenes, Aristippus, three sirens of wisdom.

The Antarctic petrel is a steadfast mate, and when one of a connubial pair is slain, the other ruefully dents the plumage of the corpse, pecking out an epitaph. If there is metempsychosis as Empedokles teaches, the albatross and the petrel are Thales and Anaxagoras.

*　　*　　*　　*　　*

Men show the smallest sense in choosing the earth they wish to sow or a suitable climate. Most of the North Americans dwell in sullen cities, and endure weather a Troglodyte in the desert would regard as unbearable. Cranes leave Scythia in winter and go to the Nile, and pelicans seek mild regions. Men are less sociable than panthers or the most rapacious wolves. Quails go in pairs and turtles in shoals, and the crow, the swan and the pelican desire companions. The solitary loses his ability to be with others, for whatever he does is for himself, which is wicked. He becomes very predacious and has a scorn for failure, and his madness for lucre is terrible. He canonizes the thief, the criminal, and simpers at justice, adultery, falsehood, and specious scales. His sole aim is itching and going some place else, and he has not the least regard for the difference between good and evil.

Who can dare give his heart to another without panting

37

with fear; for his trust bleats in his bones. The albatross sports with the frigate, the dolphin, and the shark without filling the stomach of one of his companions, and this is a proverb. He is a corpulent rover of the seas, but his belly, when opened, contains nothing but mucilage, and is the envy of Seneca.

The cinereous petrels, found in cold latitudes, also neigh, and frolic together in the evenings under the poops of ships. Some have the albic hunkers for which men sigh, and their feathers are the down of the marriage bed.

Men go everywhere looking for companions, and do not know whether they have taken unto their bosom a viper or a crow. The eagle and dragon are reliable adversaries; ichneumons hunt the caterpillar; the lark and *chloreus* eat each other's eggs; geckoes and spiders are enemies. The *pipo* devours the young of the heron. The ass frequents thorny places; Aesop and La Fontaine understood this, but few others do.

The rooks live in communes in trees, but are continually tearing up each other's nests. The English rooks, though passionate and destructive, when building nests for their young, drop enough brushwood for the poor to pick up for their hearths. There are few houses that satisfy the mind or demonstrate parental love as much as the nest of an eider. The upper part of the nest is composed of marsh-plants, and the eggs are warmed by the down the dam has pulled from her own breast.

The noise of the turtledove brings the groom to the bride, but the song of friends has gone out of the land. Few have the genius for friendship; the many are dissemblers. The recluse sits on wild stones; the monk-raven, a hermit upon inaccessible cliffs, is a bird of filth. Let not the snail or ferret nest in your soul; shun the mole, it creeps and fouls the heart. The osprey, ossifrage and eagle roost upon the head crowned with tamarisk and rushes. Do not run after unguents which the bee despises; the carancros, American vultures, exhale musk though their food is carrion. The toad destroys the honey; the *rhine* assumes the color of the rocks around it.

Those who go by the name of Filch, Cheat or Doxy, strawed and cribbed best in foreign pockets, keep their purse-droppings to themselves. They are a solitary brood though guile and hypocrisy are vastly social. The feathered brigands often associate with one another, and their spoil is common property. The pilfering stares are the companions of crows, jackdaws, and redwings. The Troupiales of the Carolinas assemble in four to five coveys to attack a larger bird, and they maintain the same martial order as they devour the prey. The wisest of men fare worse than any feathered thief. Aged Euripides, having given Athens imperishable renown, lived more alone than a cormorant. The Prometheus of Aeschylus has no companions but the elements, and the eagle, his genius, which continually devours his liver. Men are consumed by their intellects, and what pard, jaguar, or osprey could bear to be so despoiled.

Men grow degenerate far from river banks and the bulrush, or lose their song or powers without the marine bivalve, but what fowl goes alone? All that man does is to rejoin the human flock. The widgeons fly together, and gabble with one another in pools as they crop grass or fish for crabs.

Most birds live in sylvan concord with those of their own genus; some do so until one of them learns that the other has different sexual properties. There were two birds, said to belong to the order of the Capuchon-Mordore because of their monkish cowl, who occupied the same cage. Eros had almost taught them to twine their bills which they would have done were it possible. When the younger bird nuzzled close to the older, the latter clapped its wings as the damsels of Israel sounded the timbrels. Desiring to nestle they commenced to weave chickweed in the gratings of the cage. When the young one began to show the raiment of sex, the other beat and continued to persecute it until it fell down as though dead. After they were separated each one went on to make a nest which is the labor of both parents. Soon after they were apart the older bird died on a sudden, and shortly afterwards the young one perished from epilepsy.

*　*　*　*　*

Savages and birds are kinsmen; the birds of Mexico are the Chichimecas of the feathered tribes. The Aztec wore the saffron plumage of the parrot and the Xochitol, and these Mexican aborigines had as raucous a voice as that bird. The Tocolin is a brute of the forests who wears the imperial stole and breeches of Cyrus of Persia, but has no song.

The birds of New Spain wore the proud feathers coveted by the Amorite and Ashur, but they were either mute or dissonant warblers. Montezuma changed his apparel, which the parrot provided, four times a day, but he has left no hymns or poems. The canticles of the Quiché Maya and Aztecs are barbaric; Aramaic which Christ spoke resembles the wedges made by doves and gulls in sand and turf, one is the bird of Moloch and Venus, and the other belongs to the Sea of Galilee, and both wear the poor coats of fishermen.

Before *Quetzalcoatl* gave the Chichimecas and Aztecs the precious corn seeds of Tula, they ate rushes and the seeds of flowers which is the food of the Tolocatzanatl. The thrush swallows the haws of the juniper, which are so little changed when voided and dropped into the soil that they germinate. The thrush may be said to sow as he eats, but men feed without cause and gender at random.

The tops of turnips have been plucked from the craw of a ring dove and were so savory after they had been boiled as to be tender greens for the table. Would that the belly of men could provide us with such nourishment. The titlark is an artistic gourmet who will eat vermilion raisins before he will touch a white bunch of this fruit, though the latter is more succulent and sweeter. The stare haunts the reddest rose to seize the caterpillar; though he flutters about gibbets he is a mild insectivore.

The landrail is sluggish and abhors its wings, though it appears to be a disciple of Pythagoras. It is found in the cornfields, clover and among the brakes, but its craw is filled with snails. Such food is not for a warrior or a thinker. The landrail shuts its feathers when about to be taken rather than soar from the ground.

Each god, place, beauty was a bird, serpent, or animal. Paphos was the isle of Venus because it was filled with swans. Some of the rivers most precious to the mind were the Strymon, the Meander, the Cayster, the homes of this bird which represented love, hypochondria, and asceticism. Its food was often the marsh-plants and the algæ, to be seen on the banks of streams, and which bring lamentations to men.

The hierophants were called swans, and also those who were celibate recluses. Orpheus, the first poet, was related to this immaculate waterfowl, and gave up all connections with women. This infuriated the virgins and matrons of Thrace who tore his limbs apart and cast his lyre into the Hebrus.

The head of Orpheus floated upon the waters to Lemnos just as the body of Osiris rolled upon the seas to Byblus. The swan is the bird of monody, and Milton, speaking of his oary feet, calls up the image of the boat of Charon.

The swan is a primeval voyager. Content with eels and frogs, a pallet of broken reeds, or with the roofless lakes of Siberia, or the Rio de la Plata, he has the hardihood for any anabasis. Wild and migratory he is Ulysses or Xenophon, but in water close by the dwellings of men, or penned in the gravel of a yard, he pines away. Who admires geese or cranes save when they darken the clouds? Ulysses, after he has returned to Penelope and his swine, is a corpulent fateless husband. Honeycomb is in exile, hellebore is home.

Helen, born of Leda and the swan, is the most adept voluptuary of the palmated birds. Agamemnon traveled to as many foreign beds as Marco Polo journeyed to strange lands, but he was as useless to Clytemnestra as Menelaus was to Helen. Lust is the artist of beauty which was never wrought by a weak scrotum. These two sisters, Helen and Clytemnestra, pillaged Troy, sacked Menelaus, and murdered Agamemnon.

Swans are ferocious in their amours. The male swan begins by twining his neck around the female, and they remain folded together browsing upon each other's plumage until they reel. Ordinary passions come from grating, grunting, filing, sawing, flatulence, diarrhea, and catarrh, but breathing into one another's bill is Venus.

The female, once kindled, is beside herself and pursues the male swan everywhere, viewing any piece of water or clump of rushes as Solomon's bed and linen. It is told that she eats nettles to pacify her desires. The poets feign that the swan is a brutal river fowl, and that all who have that name are wicked; Cycnus, the son of Mars, was killed by Hercules because he was a robber; Cycnus, the son of Neptune, was slain by Achilles after he stabbed his mother, Philonome. The son of Apollo who had the same name was cruel. Swans would be mild were it not that birds have massive testicles.

* * * * *

The goose has not the genius of the swan. He takes less time to gender though the gander requires six geese. Among ducks the male organ of generation has a spiral shape and when it is agitated it looks as though it were an adder hanging out at the anus. The musk duck has the genitals of a Vulcan; the flavor of musk, which comes from the glands of the hunkers, arouses such senseless ardor in the drake that any hybrid or pimpled dowd among the ducks will gratify him. The duck is salacious and as desolate as Byron after Augusta has gratified him.

Don Juan burns with spleen when Astarte has exhausted him, or when she has not. After pairing the widgeon grays. The sheldrake languishes without sea salt, the mallard declines at moulting, and there is a white duck that is impotent. The drake moults shortly after mingling with the female, and at this time he paddles in the water among the mangroves at the risk of being eaten by a serpent or an alligator. The swan and the duck are not the gymnosophists of the feathered race, and they fall into as much of a passion for the fulvous neck of a female as men did to handle the bosom of Theodota.

Of all the animals man is the most easily deceived. If a goose perceives that the morning dew or rime has been brushed, he is wary. The Chinese as well as the Indians in Cuba swam in the lakes covering their heads with a calabash in which they caught the feet of the geese. The shoveler, teal,

43

pochard, widgeon, or a domesticated drake are the Judases the fowler employs to trap wild ducks. These birds are uneasy even when they see a hut which the hunter has built to conceal himself.

There is as much to be learned from a plover, sheldrake, or an eider as from Socrates or the *Laws* of Plato. What is man that he should imagine he is more than a goose? Democritus of Abdera babbled as much as any duck.

IV

BIRDS that live upon thorns do not eat worms or other living creatures, but man feeds upon everything. He is greedier for praise than the mullet and as voracious as the dolphin, and he is utterly blind to the motives of another. His food not only hurts the imagination but the affections. The Cynics carried their spare victuals in a small scrip.

It is reported that Menedemus used to give banquets to friends and passers-by, and that the second course consisted of lupines, pears, pomegranates and dried figs. This was an exceedingly moral symposium, and though there are wizened men and wights who feed as sparely, they do it solely to live longer without purpose or love or goodness.

Every sage has shown the greatest concern for what he puts into his mouth. Metrocles, the follower of Antisthenes, advised: "Gather lentils and beans, my friend." Cicero, a disciple of the teachings of the Stoa, did not eat until sundown at which time he retired to his house in the suburbs to have a meal, along with philosophic conversation with his friends. Xenophanes thought nothing so good as a meal of chickpeas, vetch and wine to ready one for talk.

Conversation is the most digestible victual; when a man talks well his friend is as responsible as he, for Aristotle, Plato, Thales, and Solon can be as empty as their companions, and nothing so exasperates a conversationalist as when his words are stupid and unwinged. Listless people can destroy the wisest faculty which is sociable, for the philosopher has the most energetic of heads, and, as Aristotle says, the energy of friendship is the basis of society.

The Cynics were often observed washing leeks in a stream and preparing vetches. One Athenian was said to eat nothing but myrtle berries, and another was supposed to have received his food from the nymphs, and it is related that he ate so little he had no evacuations. What men should eat has perplexed man as much as any other enigma. Callimachus listed the various kinds of olives with as much understanding as Homer catalogued the Greek ships at Ilium, and a good olive is as epic as the best ship, and is likely to produce a better poet. A commonwealth of intelligent feeders will not be overcome easily; a Lacedaemonian supper consisted of kidney beans and dried figs, and these were often of more service to a Spartan than the javelin and buckler.

The old poets, too, gave a great deal of attention to food; and this was a subject of vast interest to the natural philosophers. Eubulus, the poet, said the Athenian men lived on air and the sweetest hopes, and this is utopian fare, for people whose bodies are dilapidated as a result of injurious eating and flatulent living are altogether squalid, and there is no morning in their complexions; they sit sick and stand diseased. The breeze that ripens the grape disquiets their bladders, and the sun that reddens the arbutus wearies them. When the poets have indolent minds the wine-gods are human casks and vats, and the stomach, as Diogenes declares, is the Charybdis of man.

* * * * *

Democritus held that honey is good to moisten the inward parts. A stiff dry man, whether he be ascetic or not, is as much of a bane as a boring water-drinker, and either is likely to drive the young as well as the middle-aged to more lunacies than the ecstatic conjugation of turtledoves, or the belly that is a hole that can never be filled. Who does not admire Cato who had the most severe tenets and yet drank freely.

It is told that the wine is the horse of Parnassus, and Hippocrates wrote that sweet wines do not make the head heavy; he also said that water flowing from high ground and hills is the best. Hippocrates, being a healer of men, used images that clear the mind, relax the bowels, and purge the mouth.

The mother of Euripides was a vendor of herbs, and many a poet came direct from the carts and wagons of the market place in Athens. Their bucolics and georgics were table diet and medicinal recipes. Books were in good health and were as gustable as parsley, onions, or pepper. Ariadne, the Cretan maid, when left on the shore alone, fed sea swallows, and this is the damsel whom the poets eulogized and dearly loved.

May has gone out of the soul of men. This month got her name from a concubine. A plain catalogue of vegetables and herbs was considered Attic verse. Aristophanes, as jocund as the trollop of May, did not regard such a ledger-book listing as a risk. He says: "Capers, pennyroyal, thyme, asparagus, garlic, radishes, sage and rue."

Isaeus, the Egyptian Sophist, was once asked what bird or fish was the best sort of eating, and he replied, "I have ceased to take these matters seriously, for I now know that I used to feed on the gardens of Tantalus." In the days of Romulus the Pelasgians set before the gods earthen dishes filled with spelt and coarse barley. The Greeks regarded barley as the most ancient grain which they offered as sacrifices to the deities. They used to bring barley groats to Delos.

Osiris and Father Liber taught men husbandry. When men observed that the oat cricket appeared at the time when the crops began to dry, they gathered the grain. Perseus planted the first peach tree at Memphis, and the savage, weaned from his foul repasts, became frugivorous. A moiety of his river knowledge came from the spider who weaves a thick web when the waters are about to rise.

Man's cruelest enemy is his appetite which makes him envious, inconstant, hostile. Human beings are the most restive of animals, and are in a worse state than the giant with the two privy members.

The mind has increased greed and gluttony, and man's table proves that he is a manger, as Plato has remarked. The Psalmist says that man's life is brief, and yet he gives the least attention to food which is the cause of his early death. Pythagoras shunned the bean, and the lentil, and flesh, allowing his disciples fruits and herbs which would either banish dreams altogether or yield pure ones.

Human diet is foul because man eats what is available; a savage on the banks of the Niger has saner meals than civilized nations, and is content with the food, raiment, and wine of the palms; the Oritæ were fish eaters and wore the scales of those creatures.

One would imagine that man would have a low regard for himself because he has not learned to eat and void more sensibly, or to regulate his dreams. The spider drinks up the rank moisture of walls; but it is vile. The house cricket dotes on the scummings of kitchen pots, yeast and offal, which offend the imagination. The spider creeps up the tree at night to suck the eggs of the young of the hummingbird; it is loathsome. The wiles of the *Dryophis fulgida* are execrable; this pale green snake has the same colors as the foliage of the Guajara bushes where it lurks to catch tree frogs and lizards.

A poor feeder, who is not a devotee of philosophy or has no passion for the *Georgics* or the *Compleat Angler*, is parsimonious, because he does not give himself to anything, either to an abundant meal or to a poet. If he eats badly, is not a fruit and grass feeder, we remark that all he does is to distend the bulk of his oesophagus. Animals feed, gender and sleep, but have not the wonder in their gills or feet or heads that Anaxagoras had. Plato tells us that the gentle when they descend to the underworld will be translated into bees, wasps and ants, but they are more social than we are, and have more ability for friendship. Man cannot scorn the hog, for, though he roots in the mud, he dotes on figs, acorns, millet, barley, wild pears, and neither gods, nor wise beasts, nor men find this fare intolerable. The tunny eats flesh, though for the most part he lives on seaweed, and in this respect he is as much of a seer as Daniel, who, in the

Babylonian captivity, was content with pulse and water. This frugal diet prepared Daniel and his Hebrew companions for the furnace, and though friendship is a great trial and fire, few supply themselves with any viaticum for the perilous journey to another soul.

*   *   *   *   *

Plato counseled men to guard against the vices of eating, and I think he even urged people to shun fish which Aristotle thought was exceedingly fine food. Oysters are aphrodisiacs, and the dolphin is fierce, and it is possible that those that devour them acquire their traits. Since animals, clams, and polyps taught men whatever they know, the best we can do with the brains we have is to study the habits of these creatures in order to comprehend Plato.

Homer was in many ways of the mind of Socrates; the lawgiver of the Muses hated Asiatic luxury, effeminacy, and stomach-love. Priam reproaches his sons for being "the wholesale murderers of lambs and kids." When Cyclops has no men to eat he diets on curds, cheese, and milk. Nestor cuts a slice of goat-milk cheese and an onion for wounded Machaon. Homer does not give Ajax or Achilles dainty foods.

There was an epicure who is said to have eaten his meat with fingerstalls so that his food would be as warm as possible by the time he had pushed it into his mouth. Aristoxenus of the same sect as Aristippus had a cured ham named after him, which is sham immortality. Melanthius asked the gods to give him the gullet of an ostrich in order that it might take his food a long time to pass from his neck. The greedy desire exquisite and mordant joys from every part of the body, and sometimes their arms madden them, and on other occasions they swoon because of the way they

are housed in their clothes. Every pore in the skin of a hedonist is a voracious cranny, and this sieve of lust goes
about like that sloven in Athens who always had enough
obols to pay a chit, or a tart, should he happen to see one.

The infamous feeder is neither virtuous nor gentle, and the
appetite of a gourmet is a bane; Claudius doted on mushrooms, which Agrippina poisoned to despatch him; a bad
stomach is not good for wedlock, friendship, or philosophy.
The aim is not to keep men from the table or bed or to pinch
natural longings, but to caution others against the deliriums
sharpened by Aphrodite. There is no reason to rouse the
mad Muses in human beings, for man is already arrogant,
lunatic, and impious, and requires no additional instruction
in concupiscence. If he took greater care of his meals, he
would marry better, and be, as one Attic poet has said,
milder than the mallow.

Yet the gourmet enchants many persons; the sight of his
gross, amiable belly warms the clothes of dwarfed souls, and
his wines dispel the morose fogs that settle upon the solitary
bones. Nearly every one is repelled by Christ, or wormy
Lazarus, but few can resist drunken Silenus; the face flushed
with myriads of flagons pipes in all blood. The horse, growing languorous after eating heated barley, resumes a health-
ier mane when he hears the sounds of a flute.

Men gulp their good deeds as well as their vices which are
like the half-digested fish in the oesophagus of the cormorant. After people age and wax cowardly of soul, they sink
into their bellies. Old Ulysses was a glutton and not better
than the athlete Theogenes of Thasos who ate a whole bull
by himself.

After Ulysses returns to plump Penelope he is porcine.
Epaminondas, the Theban hero, said that no one ought to be

51

so fat that he could not look over his belly to see where he was passing his water. The gods have no water trouble, nor are they gross feeders, and it is said that Apollo spurned envy, an unsociable deity. Man can never attain the vision in Plato's *Republic* so long as he is incontinent, overeats, and is covetous. Ulysses comes home to his pigs and wife at Ithaca to feed and wither; for when the battle of Troy is finished Ulysses is a stomach.

Fat people are oracles of wind and water, and too steamy to converse with and are not suitable companions for a philosopher's table. It is doubtful that they are of much use to their wives, for they are too heavy for honeyed mingling because their bellies get in the way of the parts they wish to employ.

THE FIRST MORTALS were content in swamp and reed. The herbs of the marsh and dog's-tooth grass were bread. Sidon and murex and Arabic alabaster were unknown. The seasons were no more than a matter of winds. Men were plants and the cowries of the shore, and woman a potherb, her legs and hair were rain. River rushes, fennel stalk, the dusk were the odors of apples and desire.

Salt pools were the eyes and head of man, his verteber was a tidal seam; the marshes dreamed, the dunes thought; Ocean, swamp and sands were in his mind and visage; he had no wish to grasp them because he had no feet or hands, the malign tutors of greed and strife. The small stones slept near him as lambs. Sea and quagmire, kelp and cockle were mother and father, and Abel, who is feeling.

*   *   *   *   *

Most enquiring minds are ever trying to learn how men were in the beginning. They have the same elation that was Alexander's when he saw crocodiles in the River Hydaspes and Egyptian beans in the Acesines, imagining he had discovered the source of the Nile. Paradise is what is First; Alpha, or Albic; the primeval mists, or the white stole of God. Aristophanes claimed there were at first three sexes, man, woman, and man-woman. This creature was round and he had eight limbs; his back and sides were a circle, and he had two faces. The monster had four ears and two privy members, and he rolled everywhere. He had no need to couple with another because he was altogether self-sufficient, although it is hard to understand how he connected his two parts. These androgynous creatures did not impregnate each other, but sowed their seed in the ground like grasshoppers. Having four ears, eight limbs, and two private parts made them fierce and arrogant, for it is doubtful whether any of the gods were so fortunate. Zeus decided to split the man-woman into two, for the giant with the double organs despised the gods, and had scorn for the universe and the animals in it. The brutes, too, before the days of Deucalion had titanic genitals, but these beasts were not hermaphrodites and could hardly rival the human giants. Zeus bade Apollo to reshape man, and he took the generative organs which were behind and put them in front, which was a cosmical error, for what man sees arouses him.

It was the belief of ancient annalists that men had far larger bodies than now, and that there were giants in the earth in the first days, when there was much more vapor, emptiness, and sea than earth. Nature then produced monstrous creatures that had the breasts, the neck and the head of men but whose lower parts were those of a sea creature. Theophrastus held that in the beginning man was a fish and like any other animal; the human infant was suckled at the breasts of the shark. Water came long before fire and stones. There were creatures also with the faces of huge fish that had one ear and an unparted lip and which lived by smelling pot-herbs and air. Saint Augustine reports that in his own time he saw on the shore of Utica a man's axle-tooth that was equal in size to a hundred of ours.

Nature created many monsters, some without mouths, others neckless. Hesiod affirms that there were webfooted men, and Saint Augustine writes that there were unipeds who slept under the shade of their foot. Strabo, Diodorus and Pliny were of the mind that there were people with baboon faces, and Augustine speaks of the Cynocephali that had dog's heads and barked. Nature was and is still at work on the shape of the races, and there is small doubt that men are dwindling in stature and in procreative strength. Homer sorrows over the depleted energies and size of man. Hector, Ajax and Nestor, who came long after the Deluge, were inferior to the first children of Adam.

Though there is a record of the first men in *Genesis*, they do not appear to have talked or gendered. Before Adam, man was in part stone, demon and brute. The Tree of Good and Evil bears the fruit of knowledge and shame. In Ezekiel this beautiful being has the round soles of a calf, proving that man is in greatest part a pure, visionary animal. Jared, Mahalalel and Methuselah begat without the assistance of the female, and these immense mastodons had no minds or privy organs, or any knowledge of their uses. Vice and coupling take a long time to understand, and though Adam and Eve preferred the Tree of Good and Evil to the fruits of infinite life, they showed themselves to one another without having sexual intercourse. Their great sin was in learning that they were naked, and this gave them boundless joy. Men learned to copulate from the angels that entered the daughters of men, and their issue were giants, who, being amorous beasts with human parts, were confused and stupid, because it is the mind in man that baffles the animal in him.

Woman was taken from Adam when he slept which shows that man and woman were originally one and that the greatest mistake that nature has committed was to divide man from woman, for what Adam originally had in himself he later had to pursue.

Unlike man at present, neither Methuselah nor Lamech wore out their parts in the first sixty years. There are many causes for the ebbing of human force in the earth: according to Philo, Cain was a profligate, and all malcontents are licentious. Human skin arouses lascivious aches, for the Greeks held that the original man was enclosed in a prickly bark.

*   *   *   *   *

At first man was mist and sea water, but as he was clothed with flesh he imagined he was beautiful, and it is said that Lamech, who was seventh from Adam, had a daughter, Naamah, which is interpreted as "beautiful pleasure." Pleasure came very soon into man's mind, and Methuselah and Mahalalel lived very long because they neither thought nor had lusts. Philo writes that Adam signified virgin red clay, and he partook of the Tree of Knowledge, or Lust, which bears the fruit of death. Knowledge brings confusion which begets lechery. Adam was virgin ground so long as he did

56

not look at himself, but when he did, he grew shameful organs. Soon as man sees himself he waxes vain and desires to be a first cause. Adam did not mingle with woman until later, for it is said that before Seth was born he bare stones which is what the vestal earth does.

What is the ultimate form or the divine shape of future man? Augustine says that at Hippo there was one born with feet and hands like half moons. There are numerous hermaphrodites in the world, and we consider these nature's mischances, but they doubtless existed millions of years ago, and disappeared, and now on occasion appear again. There were persons who had both sexual properties, and according to Augustine, this double creature was able to beget children out of one body. Whether these are prodigies or marvelous births that are of the generation before the Flood we do not know.

It would appear bizarre to assert that man in the future will have no tongue, ears, mouth, or excrements, were there not fish and testacea who are the Seraphim men have imagined.

Man is unreasonable, and his sanity hangs by the thread of Ariadne. Doing wrong is one of his daintiest satisfactions, and harming another is as exquisite an ecstasy as coition. Man cannot endure his own vices in others, and he cannot overcome himself enough to pardon a friend whom he has injured. Proteus does not change his shape any more often than man or the earth which is primeval chaos. Human beings have not attained their ultimate shape, any more than the Cordilleras of Mexico and the Andes, which are unstable, fiery Vulcans, sterile summits, which in thousands of years will be ocean bottom where the race of Nereus will rove once more.

The human race has declining powers, and man resembles

less the brute the more he approaches what we define as mind. He is in an intermediate form; the highest man will have no scrotum; it is ludicrous for a moral philosopher to scrape and scratch as any worm. Euripides was a misogynist, but Sophocles said that though he hated women in his Tragedies, he found them rapturous creatures in his bed.

Man is at present in a misshapen stage, neither possessing the gentler customs of the beast, nor the faculties of the angel.

In some men the weasel is dominant, and in others the osprey, or the sloth, but he is weaker than most animals, and he is ruttish in all seasons.

Aborigines are the kinsmen of hills, larks, vales, woodlands; the kings of Alba bore the surname of Sylvius because the son of Ascanius was by chance born in the forests. Early in the annals of men the races are confounded; towns are of riffraff origin, and are spawned rather than formed. Romulus, desiring to gather enough people together for a Latin commonweal, set up a primitive sanctuary fenced round with briars and brambles to which thieves, the rabble, and violent fugitives from neighboring towns could repair as to a refuge.

It is impossible to predict the metamorphosis of human beings. Man in his present state has as much desire to urinate as he has to make vows to Artemis. He is still in a primeval condition, and is very inferior to the Mountain that spoke to Moses. Most of his knowledge is shared by the kite, and the shark and the spider. Though Lot was one of the last of the just men in Sodom, he lay with his two daughters and was as easily captured as the viper after drinking a vessel of wine left in a hedgerow by a hunter.

Lamech bare sons that were harpers, braziers and children

who made tents of the hair's cloth of libertine goats; fullers and potters were lechers; Cain was a carpenter and the stones of his house fell upon him and killed him. Others say that blind Lamech, the father of artisans, slew Cain. There were also the women who worked at the spinning wheel who were lascivious, for they put their foot to the treadle, the motion of which kindles many secret passions. Penelope was a seamstress, and many of the poets of the Greek Comedy believed that she was unchaste. Dekker, much later, in recounting the profligates of London, mentions chapmen, maltmen, vintners.

God shrive the artisans Tubal-Cain, Gale and Garge, the patriarchs of the tambourine, corn grinder and the axe.

Only when the leek, the cucumber, onion, mushroom, and the Egyptian bean were cultivated did man come to carnal knowledge. This was after the Deluge when Ham was the first to observe his father's nakedness. Ham and his son Cush were the original artists, for painting is all about the nudity of other people and ourselves.

*　*　*　*　*

All flesh is trouble; if one bridles his feet and hands he is unable to tether his lips, and even when one avoids putrid food, he may smell. Every one in Athens shunned a pair of philosophical water-drinkers because of their bad odor.

In Eden there are two trees: "Behold, I have set before thy face life and death, good and evil: choose life." Every Prophet has perished, for if man eat of the Tree of Knowledge he will die, and the Angel with the flaming sword that guards the Tree of Life can never be overcome until men are of a different shape, substance, and mind. The fable reads that the men at Babel had one lip and a single voice, but that God confused them, giving them a double mouth, and many voices. Many stars will dim, and planets go to their doom, and oceans sorrow, before the human race can attain one sublime identity. When the two-headed animal that writes strays from the haunts of Artemis, the river gods, and the precincts of Thoth, he is the lawless goat.

THE MYTH GATHERERS

VI

MAN is always seeking Eden, and the geographers of Paradise have named the rivers and located the blessed ground where Adam and Babylonian Gilgamesh dwelt. In the beginning there were cockle, scoriæ, sea lava; the onyx, jacinth, emerald of Elysium resemble Ecbatna, the summer site of Semiramis, rather than the primordial earth of the crustacea that inhabited the great waters. When nature wears scoriæ and igneous rock, she is the maiden, and her matrix is holy.

All men hunger for Alpha. Ptolemy titled *terra incognita*, Albion, which he imagined existed far beyond the Western Ocean. On his apocryphal map this was First Land, the immaculate continent, more suitable as the white stole of God than as cartography. The first shall be last, and the last shall be first is geologic scripture. The extinct, coastal bivalves which form the wet desolate cliffs of *Tierra del Fuego*, or the Straits of Magellan, more akin to Void than Eden, belong to what is first. In the beginning there was NO-THING before which the Angels fled.

Europeans came to the Americas for a new energy; Hercules had set up the Pillars as a barrier to the geographer and the soul. The Atlantic was the Sea of Darkness, and he who went over these watery plains had as his pilot, Charon.

Man is a dropsical animal, more water, sleep and death than any other element. Water is the lodestar of man; the Ocean contains seers we know not. In the seas all philosophies are writ; 'tis an empty bosom the fool may aver, but of such folly was the world created.

Of pelagic origin we are the children of bays and rivers, and Ocean draws more sighs and vaster ruins than the stars. The geographer cannot slake his soul at home; sea water kills the drinker, but not his fate; of marine salt is destiny wrought.

Orphans of Tyre and Utica, man-slaying skalds from the Hebrides, the Norsemen ranged icy Blacksark and tread the Virginia humus in beast's shoes and untied latchets, howling for threshold and kindred. They were a race of castaway Cains; a freebooter was Thorfinn the skull-killer; Eric was sent out from *Haukadal* to *Nod*; witch and bed was Thorbiorg, gloved in catskin; from the loins of Gudrid issued Iceland; the walrus tusk garnished her knife; an Arctic fox was Freydis; her breasts gave suck to swords. The hill, ravine and hummock were their book of lineage; the Chickahominy waters sired the savage; in the River *Panuncks* flowed his name; maize, gourds, squash, pumpkins familied the Indian. Each reed or osier was Abel or Seth to seafaring waif, widow or Indian vestal. Iceland is honest saga and farmstead; *Vinland* is the polar grape of Jericho, but Greenland, a tumulus in the sea, is Red Eric's fable and perjury.

The realm of Florida went as far north as the imaginary, congealed gates to Cathay. Cabot was supposed to have viewed this land when he was off the headlands of Labrador. Mariners have asserted that a Floridian bay flowed inland for three hundred leagues, and was a sporting ground for whales.

The Atlantic voyager was a gatherer of havoc; greed was his polestar, but his watery roots were his unknown quest. Florida was the empery of the Conquistador. This region extended from the land of Cod south to Powhatan's Virginia, and included Carolina, Georgia, Alabama, and as far west as the fatal river-grave of De Soto, and the *Rio Palmas*, which is the *Rio Grande* River.

The booty of the Spanish was the discovery of a new earth, the annals of which are our legends and gospels. Small worth to them were the sweet acorns of the oak in the desert of Cíbola, which when pounded was Indian bread. What profit had Solomon of his wisdom, or they in learning that between *Sonora* and *Suya* the natives drank wine made of a great thistle, and that watercress grew in the springs in the wilds of *Chichilticalli*, or that the ravined riverbanks were heavy with pennyroyal, marjoram and a fruit, kindred to the rose bush, which had the odor of muscated grapes.

*　*　*　*　*

The European succumbed to the new continent; it was sterile earth which brewed fatal ends. Indian earth was a negative Golgotha. Martina Carvalho, a Portugal, went with over two hundred men in quest of gold which is almost as indestructible as avarice. They came upon a crystal mountain, and then saw a river between two mountains which shone like the stones of Ophir. They bit the grains with their teeth to determine whether it was a precious metal. In desert country their sustenance was some grass; one day they caught a snake upon which they supped. Sick and fearful of the red savages, they turned back in canoes, going on the river *Cricare;* in a rapid, the canoe containing the gold was lost. After eight months of starvation, they returned to *Porto Seguro* utterly poor, their hopes dead.

The Spanish hidalgo and Portugal adventurer came for riches, but the harvest was often no more than the piñon nut, tanned hides of the woolly cattle of the Platte, or virgin discovery, which, like learning, is tombstone destiny.

Ginger, cassia, storax paint the Moluccas in the blood, but Magellan's men are glyphed bones at the Popinjays. Gathering wrack in the windy Magellans, the sole lodestar of sea-worn hearts was their daughters of Cadiz, and entering a wild tract of water, named it the Strait of the Eleven Thousand Virgins.

Beneath the crust of the Christian was the new earth and river heathen. The explorers found feral ground that slaked their own natures. One ransacking customs to understand man is no less baffled than Montezuma was when seeing Cortes and his soldiers kneeling to the Rood, asked why they humbled themselves before an ordinary tree.

There were many martyrs of Canada and Florida, and the streams and towns that bear their names seem as legendary as the numerous towns of Jason that are everywhere in Armenia and in Media. The sea brigands who drowned in the Florida tides or in the Iroquois wilderness are as renowned as Juba, Ptolemy and Aristotle; they were no worse than

66

Jason who was said by some to have gone far up the Ister, or even into the Exterior Sea. The Argonautic expedition was no less real than the fleets of Cristóbal Colon, or Sir Walter Raleigh's quest for the Elysian plains in Brazil.

The corsairs of Jason who learned navigation from Aeolus came to America for the Golden Fleece, but most of them died mad or drowned in storms off the Bahamas. Magellan, bringing the Christian cross to the Moluccas, was a lunatic pirate; Frobisher was as covetous as Cacus whom Hercules subdued.

The Spanish *Caballero* had an indomitable character, and good or evil, that is the ore of Prometheus and myth-gatherers. De Soto's men, steeped in the gall and hyssop of the American forest, made saddles out of the ash tree, and they cut off the noses and hands of Indians because war and bloodshed were their main entertainments. After three years in the wilderness, De Soto's remains were lowered in the hollow of a tree bark into the waters of the Mississippi. His goods, sold at public outcry, consisted of five Indian slaves, three horses, and seven hundred swine. Cortes had pillaged ancient Aztec sepulchres for gold. But all this was to be, no matter who the discoverers were. When the Portugals came to the Azores, meaning goshawks, the birds had no fear of men, whom they had never seen. The Indians, for the same reason, were no less hospitable. This is the way of man, and neither Solomon nor Aristotle has changed him. The Spaniards, disciples of Ptolemy, Pliny and Marco Polo, could be no better than humanity. They were amazing geographers, and they left chronicles, bought at the price of an entire race, which is leafy and perishable, but history is not. In the fifteenth century there were maps of the entire earth carved in brass and pewter that were as wondrous as Achilles' shield. Centuries earlier Charlemagne sat at a silver table upon which the world was engraved.

The land is still unclaimed and unsettled, and the wild ground waits for the mattock and the hoe, and the love, which is genius, to make it an epic furrow, house and hearth.

Our forefathers were giant volcano-horses; America was not earth as the elephant-shaped mounds in Kansas show. The great, grassy basin, the Catskill eagle made us tribal and fierce; the Pawnee, leading the sorrel of the Platte by a bull-hide rope, lessoned us in poverty, for Want is a tough, rude god made out of dried buffalo skin, to which we must kneel and pray, lest we perish of sloth and satiety. Men are milder on their knees, but ever chaffering with doom, grimaced by chance. We have lost the ground, city-cursed that we are, left it behind us like the *Quiché* did the *Yaqui* for whom they wept.

Return to the Platte, the bison, the hoofprints of the deer, for we are as hungry for them as the wandering *Quiché*, who had to smell the points of their *Ceiba* staffs to deceive their empty stomachs.

Whatever we do is vast, unconscious geography; we are huge giants of the mesa. The prairie is still an altar for the coyote and Ishmael.

VII

THE ALPHEUS no longer contents the mind; when the sheep drink of the waters of the Cephisus they turn white; it is told that mares pastured by the Astaces which is on the Black Sea suckle their foals with jetty milk. The mind sorrows and frets as much as corrupt flesh, and neither ancient prodigies can satisfy the one any more than Helen or Dido or Medea can ease or keep quiet the other. Nature takes its revenge upon the intellect because the body cannot rest; the intellect can only quell matter in different places and worlds, or tutor the feet when disease and dotage confine restive man.

All the errors concerning the human race come from not realizing that man is merely another animal. There is no beast as bored as man; tedium is his worst affliction, and the root of nearly all his amusements. He is valorous in sorrow, and the reason that he is most resolute in war and during plagues is that he has a negative genius.

Let no one assume that the fables of the red races of the three Americas do not invigorate the intellect. The legends are vast energies to be domesticated; the continent is a prone mongol Titan, with the jaw of Osiris.

The minds of men differ little from the estuaries, the ravine stones, the fens near where they dwell. Savage ground bears men of water and stone. The Navajo said that the first man came out of the ground as a moth-worm. The Inca said the moon appeared first at *Lake Titicaca*. The holy mountain of *Tonacatepec* was the source of all the rivers of the earth. The *Wichita* mountains were the progenitor of the tribe of that name. The Egyptians say that the swamp fathered men in the beginning, and that they ate bread made of a bog root. Murex is found on the rocks at Gaetulia, and it is said that scorpions cannot live at Clupea. There is the forest intellect, and the mind sown by ocean winds. Some people have water souls, and are fisher- or boatmen, and they handle the oar. Other persons are tubers, or rough laurel flowers. Each has as his muse a tree, rain, or the humid leaves.

The American intellect is a placeless hunter. It is a negative faculty which devours rather than quiets the heart. *Dakotah* is an Indian word for friend though it is a cruel tribe. This is a battle and prairie mind. Its deity is not Christ, but *Quetzalcoatl*, who is wind and snake; and its travail is as fierce as that of the Indian woman who cannot bring forth until she is given the blood of the serpent.

The Indian, or American mind, is primal rather than domestic because it is new; the circle was known to the North American savages; the *Quiché Maya* in the *Chilam Balam* tell of the Father of the Kosmos grasping in his hand a stone sphere which set the four winds in motion. One of the gifts of Montezuma to Hernando Cortes was two round emblems in gold and silver representing the sun and the moon, but the wagon or wheel was lost long before the Tolteca and the Inca.

The American fable is a table of the seasons, the moons, days and annals of the pilgrimages of tribes. The Aztecs lamented their separation from *Tulan* so bountiful in maize, gourds, flowers and cacao, but their gods had no concern with human fate, or for the wounds that come from perfidy, chance, or from the decay of symbols.

Whether the lore of the Americas is as antique as Isis, which means ancient, is in great doubt. Indian myths are the dregs of Asian lore; Greek legends are no more than Nile debris; the Arcadians claimed to be older than the moon, but how ancient are the red races? The *Muyscas* say that they inhabited South America before the moon accompanied the earth; the Semitic races wandered as far as the mouth of the Indus, and yet this does not resolve the enigma of the redskinned children. The Indians of the Middle America have a strong Pacific nature, and yet *Quetzalcoatl* or *Kukulcan* was not a Mongol, but fair of skin, and bearded. These were few in numbers compared to the hordes that came from Siberia or the countries of the Scythæ or Tartars; they were flat of brow, the mouth of savage will, the eyes of China, but the jaw was European.

These new people, scorified remnants of Tartary and Tibet, had a jaguar *Genesis*. The Quiché Maya call their books *Chilam Balam*, or the Scriptures of the Jaguar Priest,

71

and this is barbaric awe and theogony. Baal is a Phoenician idol, and a god of the Mayans. Aristotle relates that so many people from Carthage, who had formerly come from Sidon and Tyre, had departed for a continent beyond the Pillars, that a rigorous law was passed to prevent these Phoenicians from leaving and depopulating their homeland.

Diverse continents gender dissimilar intellectual properties; and the *Chilam Balam* of the Quiché Maya is a beast psalm; the Egyptian *Book of the Dead*, the *Gilgamesh Epic*, and the fables of the Aztec and Quiché Maya were conceived in the head of the crocodile, the bull of Ashur and the American coyote. But the papyrus lying between the knees of a Pharaoh, laden with mumia and honey, contained vows and affections not to be found in the rituals of the New World.

It is the works and produce of nature in America and not of man at which we marvel. The rituals of the table, the bed, and the hearth were never established; the naphtha that flows wild from South American rocks was burnt in the lamps at Genoa; Medea, lacking the knowledge of the turtledoves of Mylitta or Ashtoreth, destroyed her rival, the daughter of Creon, in the flames of naphtha.

Man is at the nadir of his strength when the earth, the seas, the mountains are not in him, for without them his soul is unsourced, and he has no images by which to abide.

Much of the Americas was dead ground. The mountains about the Strait of Magellan are hopeless land; close by is Port Famine, and St. Julian, another fatal harbor, is a scaffold in the minds of men. The Strait is cool in summer, where wild horses graze on fungus. *Tierra del Fuego* is miserable, rainy coast though called the land of fire. The wretched Patagonian shingle was formed of extinct shells that were several millennia ago crustacea on the floors of the sea. The savages of this region live on the fungus and the berries from the humpback arbute, and eat the old women when there is a poor harvest of these outcast roots and fruit. Northern Siberia is frozen country, and the islands lying in the near-by sea are composed of the carcasses of elephants and rhinoceroses. These congealed, pachydermatous islets are memorials of torrid heat, the summer olive and the parrot. We underestimate the dead, who bequeath to us their sorrows and knowledge, and also their bodies. Lichen may be seen sprouting on a mule's bones. How long is it between the Patagonian fungi, the wild celery whose furrow is a bald cairn of shellfish, and the warm grass of Guatemala that mothered maize?

Maize, like the fig of Asia Minor, or the fragrant rice fields of Ceylon, is a tutored stalk of civilized peoples. *Quetzalcoatl* instructed the Aztecs to offer hyacinths and copal to their idols instead of human flesh.

The *Orinoco*, the *Rio Negro* and Indian land are not to be mistaken for the holy Pison; Sir Walter Raleigh sought the carbuncles, emeralds, and the gold of Eden in the woody swamps of the *Muyscas* rumored to be *El Dorado*. The rocks of St. Paul, though they be as white as the Angel Uriel or the stars, owe their immaculate stole to the dung of sea fowls. The sea slug feeds on kelp in shoaly water, but who will address this creature as Poseidon?

Man is still a rude geologist, and knows as little of the entrails of the earth as he does of man. Diodorus assures us that the Atlantides had no knowledge of the uses of corn because they were already a remote people before Osiris had taught the Egyptians how to plant the barley, oats, and corn seeds. The ancient Jews claim that the original groats in the ground were a particle of God's body. *Quetzalcoatl* taught the Mexicans the uses of maize, but this Caucasian hero, shipwrecked on the sunrise slopes of Mexico, lost his own memory; the lava craters of the Mexican *Cordilleras*, the pillars of cactus, and the thorny mimosas were far from the Mount of Olives and the Gardens of Galilee.

VIII

THE ANCIENT MEXICANS were a gross lake people; they were water sorcerers. Mud and reeds was their place of habitation, and water made them as deceitful and brutish as the *Chichimecas* who plucked up trees as though they were lettuce stalks. Their idol *Vitzliputzli* made them wanderers.

The first tribes that arrived in New Spain came from the Seven Caves; they were the *Chichimecas* who were Cyclops, the *Ottomies*, the *Navatalcas* who had a polite speech, and the *Suchimilcos* who were seeded by flowers and inhabited the banks of the lakes; the *Tepanecans* had a *curaca* named after an ant's nest which is found in huge, moist hillocks. Then came the *Tlalluicans*, a rude tribe of the Sierra whose lord was *Quahunachua*, now Cuernavaca. The men of bread were the *Tlascaltecans* who built *Tlascala*. Those from the Seventh Cave were the Mexicans who carried *Vitzliputzli* in a coffer of reeds. This idol promised the Mexican wanderers copal, the balsam of the vineyards of Engedi, silver, gold, turquoise, and the feathers of the macaw as their raiment. They came to *Mechovacan* which breeds many lakes and abundant fish, where they built a house for *Vitzliputzli*, and sowed Indian wheat and pulse. Of the Seven Cave nations, they were the last to people cities and sow maize.

Mamre is known as the vale of tears because Adam wept there, but the Valley of Mexico is the place of the skulls. The passions of nations would lead them to the *Psalter*, or to that vast plain watered by the Jordan and canonized by the bones of Job, were it not that man is mad.

The amorous apples of Haran did not grow on the Mexican lava hills and slopes of Scoriæ. Mire was their home, water their hope and desolation. The Mexicans left a remnant of their tribe at *Malinalco* because they were crones and wizards. They longed to dwell among the reeds in *Tula*, but *Vitzliputzli* forbade it. They changed the course of a great river so that it coiled around *Coatepec*, a small hill, forming a lake that nurses savines, willows, elms, and many fish. Their god commanded them to leave *Tula*, and those who did not obey the idol were found dead in the morning; their stomachs had been opened, and the hearts pulled out of the corpses. This was the labor of *Vitzliputzli* who from that time demanded human sacrifice of the Mexicans.

* * * * *

Copil was the son of the Mexican hag of the Muses, Malinalco, for art is sorcery. He was slain and cast into *Lake Acopilco*, and out of his heart leaped the cactus sword, the

76

bloody plant of Montezuma and Mexi, the lord of the hordes from whom the Mexicans derived their name. The intellect is a bird of rapine; Philo regarded the angels as a sign of contemplation; the cherubim of Ezekiel are great winged birds of thought. The intellect in the New World is the eagle, and the Muses are wild earth. *Tenochtitlan* was built upon a stone where the cactus sprouts and the eagle sits.

The lake in which *Tenochtitlan* stood was sloughy and malodorous, and the Mexicans were in sore need of water to drink. After Autzol, their eighth king, was elected, he called one of his soothsayers to alter the course of a river so that it would enter the city. Manco Capac had cast a hollow cane into a channel to make the water flow, and Moses hurled the bough of an almond into the brook called Mareh, the Hebrew word for bitter waters, after which it was sweet and potable. Only the profane are indifferent to the rivers in the earth, which slake the thirst of the cosmographer.

When the bed of the great stream had been bent so that it brought a current of clear water into the Mexican lake, the wizards cast incense on its banks, sacrificed quails, and sounded coronets.

The names of the Mexican kings, and their lineage are a register of their customs. Their origins were plain and strong, for as Thucydides remarks, a people in their beginnings show remarkable energy; what often repels us is not entirely wicked, since everything that man does, when recollected, is a marvelous legend.

The original towns were of wattled mud and weeds, and their first king was Acamapixtli, which is the Mexican name for a few reeds. The one who succeeded him was called Rich Feathers, or Vitzilovitli. Of the tail and wing of the parrot and the macaw they wrought garments of as many colors as Joseph's coat. Birds were Indian gods and seasons; there were tame ravens in a temple on the California coast, and in the equinoctial lands the macaw represented summer and the raven winter. The flesh of the parrot was a Mexican table delicacy, and the aboriginal Aztecs ate mountain cats, tigers, and the puma which has the flavor of veal. When Cortes came to *Tenochtitlan* a small breed of dog was not only an immense delight to the Indians, but the Spaniards considered this animal as savory as a pheasant. It takes a savage as long to become civilized as it does a European from Toledo or the River Europas to become a rank thinker and feeder.

They also had Chimalpopoca for king, which means a Flaming Target, and then Izcoalt whose ancestor was a snake. When they elected a new king they drew blood from his ears and legs with the talons of a griffin, and they anointed him with the unction of the dead; some of the tribes derived their ointment from the oil of salamanders and vipers.

The last free king of the Mexicans was Montezuma, who told Cortes, his conqueror, that he made war upon his neighbors to exercise the people, which is what Plato had in mind, because idle citizens are insane men. Montezuma was grim of visage, and, as his appellation suggests, was a tyrant. No plebeian might look him in the face, and whenever a stranger defiled the air he occupied, his attendants fumigated him with incense.

Nations can expire of surfeit in fifty years. Montezuma was as much given to copal and the perfume of flowers as King Midas, who, after debauching his realm, offered Zeus his father's farm wagon.

Montezuma was as melancholy and as pusillanimous as Saul, and consulted witches every day long after he had heard of the arrival of Cortes whom he thought was the white-skinned *Quetzalcoatl*, god of *Cholula*. When his messengers returned from the camp of the Spaniards with a rich cloth on which were painted the ships and men of Cortes, he sacrificed a number of Indians and sprinkled their blood on these ambassadors, which was done when good tidings were received. Men endeavor to change their fate, for whether it is good or bad, they find it insupportable. Heliogabalus had the same need to swindle destiny and his assassins; he thought he could rob them of their joy, and that he would die as he wished. He sweetened his pond with roses so that, should they drown him in it, he would expire perfumed. He prepared a halter of twisted silk were he to hang; should he be stabbed he made ready a bodkin of gold, or could he avoid them altogether, he secreted poison in a box made of the unicorn. He died standing up to his chin in a privy, showing only his head, which was sufficient for his murderers.

Some say Montezuma was killed by a stone thrown by one of his vassals; others claimed that Cortes slew him; whatever his end was, his servant took his ashes and buried them in a contemptible place.

* * * * *

The Aztecs were as sensual as flowers; each of the eighteen months of the Mexican zodiac was a sign for maize, squash, sun and gore. The days were governed by the tiger, ape, and rain. Like the Tibetans, the Aztecs had five suns or catastrophes which destroyed the human race. One of these cycles began on the day for tiger, for those who did not perish by famine were eaten by tigers. They were the most cultivated cannibals in the world; the Indian hedonist slew people as though they were dahlias and poured forth their blood as if they were drawing out the odor of mountain clover. Had they but eaten their gods instead of men, they would have been Gymnosophists or Pythagoreans, or one of the great symbolic peoples of the earth. Copal, the plumeria, their carnal flower, mountain tigridia, suffocated the Mexican to death.

They had Levitical wizards in their temples, the stones of which were hewn into snakes and snails; they cast incense on *Vitzliputzli* at daybreak, at noon, at sunset and at midnight, after which they beat themselves or drew blood from their legs with an obsidian dagger. There were the virginal boys, like the Inca vestals, who cleansed the floors and altars with the temple besom. These acolytes gathered scorpions, palmer worms, and spiders, of which they made an ointment for their gods.

Some of the priests who hated the human pudenda cast them away, but after that they flayed as many hapless slaves as before. Seneca writes of a man who constuprated a pair of wenches in a night, and since men are far more lewd than logical, we scorn the Aztec spado, and marvel at this deed of rapine.

The Mexican man-eaters were vegetable symbolists; their capes were made of the maguey root, and with the thorns of this plant the penitents pierced their sinning tongues. Like Empedokles, who made sacrificial kine out of myrrh and frankincense, the Aztecs wrought their deities out of corn paste, amaranth seeds, and beans. Venus was sea scum and *Vitzliputzli* was an image made of the paste of seeds, maize and honey.

War was the religious amusement of the Mexicans, and

whenever they were in battle they rested every fourth day, which is the same custom the ancient Jews practiced as they would not fight against the Romans who besieged Jerusalem on their Sabbath. The Aztecs engaged in hostilities with nations to acquire captives for their oratories and their table. Water was their dwelling place, and blood nourished their lake lilies and rites.

Aztec art so admired as primitive was sanguinary. No forest or *Rio Negro* alligator or jaguar was the peer of the Aztec priest who cast incense to the four winds attired in the skin of a human victim.

The Aztec worked with the feathers of the parakeet; he was a lapidary in turquoise, an artisan in metals. His art was conceived in the head of the puma, the jaguar, the coyote, whose bones were interred with the remains of a mother or father. Art is a *huaca* with the belly of Moloch.

The Aztecs had numerous *Tlalocs*, or rain, thunder, and weather deities; *Tecutli* governed the four cardinal points, and gave the matmakers the fat reeds they needed. They made vows to their mountains, and moulded images in the shape of men to represent *Popocatepetl, Iztac Tepetl,* and the summits of *Poiauhtecatl.* The Inca took faggots and clothed them as people to be slain; they also flung into the coals of the brazier tallow, maize, opulent raiment, and children. In the month of *Atl Caualo* the Mexicans killed many children on the mountain peaks; this was the time when new fires were prepared, and the food for the Aztec Moloch was carried to its hapless end in a litter, followed by singing and dancing throngs, strewing flowers as they went.

The feast days of the Mexicans were Sabbaths in Tartarus. They had an idol of repentance, *Tezcallipuca,* who pardoned them every four years for their sins, and a god,

Tlaloc, who gave them rain. The penitent trembled before *Tezcallipuca* who wore a jewel that covered his rank belly, and a greenstone at his navel. He was the Baal of the Mexican Golgotha, wrought of the heads of dead men.

Man-eating is the custom of all peoples, and it is better to sacrifice men to an Aztec idol with eyes of squash and teeth of beans for symbols than to do it as a liar, a hypocrite and for greed. It is not good for the man or woman offered to the gods to appease the blood, but it is better for humanity.

The annuity that the king paid to Cristóbal Colon for discovering a route to Cathay came from the taxes imposed upon the butchershops of Seville. This is a doleful reminder that the Christian is as much of a carnivore as any Indian flesh-eater.

The Inca and Aztec took the same pious care with the human flesh they offered to the idols as the Jews did with a ram or sheep brought to the altars of Elohim. The young victim was without a blemish; his teeth were as white as the sea conch; were his fingers stupid or obese, or if his navel hung, he was given brine to drink that he might become lean. At the feast of *Toxcatl* the victim went through the village sounding the flute and wearing jocund flowers; the palsied or lame children came to touch him and throw away their diseases. For twenty days he was Faustus, having four Indian Dianas, as virginal as woodland laurel, for his pleasure. Then, after the Aztec Faustus had come to the end of his days as a voluptuary, he broke his flute, and before he ascended the steps of the temple, *Tlacochalco*, the four Indian women wept and departed. When he reached the summit of the oratory, the priest plunged the obsidian knife into his breast, tore out the embered heart and raised it aloft to the sun.

* * * * *

During the feast of *Vitzliputzli* the priest came out of the temple in a surplice that fell as far as his hams, sounding an earthen fife which made every murderer, thief and adulterer shake. In Peru and Mexico adultery was punished by death, for no one wants to be taken for a cuckold, a title which would not create so much mockery were men not droll animals.

The mother of the gods was *Teeu Innan*, also called *Toci*; she was the spindle and broom deity, and the mummers at her feast wore nothing but a rope for a clout. The old men sang for her and beat a turtle-shell drum. *Tlacotteutl* was a divine woman who represented human perversity. This is a malign goddess who rules everybody. Paul relates in the *Epistle to the Romans* that whatever he resolved to do, he seldom did. Most men, unable to endure their own lot, are ecstatic when others are galled; some attempt to bring harm to whole races of people by deriding their saints, or belittling Gethsemane or Moses on the rock, Choreb. It is alleged that one of the nails driven into the hands of Jesus was hammered into a horse's bridle for the emperor of Constantinople.

On some of their holidays, when *Ixcuiname* is celebrated, the Aztec starved his entrails. They held holy meals for *Chicome Coatl* who told them about quail-colored beans, the amaranth, and foods. They decked this idol in a shirt of the colors of a ripe lime, orange, or white maize blossoms. For the feast of *Tezcatlipoca* they chose a captive to be slain.

Work, penance, art and festivals were mingled. When there was drought, the priests of the *Tlalocs* fasted, abstained from women and offered copal to the gods so that the rains would come. During the rain festival, which took place in the sixteenth month, they made images of their mountains.

Uixtociuatl, adorned with squash blossoms, was their salt goddess. The people came from the marshes wearing wormwood flowers in their hair, and they sang and danced ten days for salt. At the end of their dances and orisons another became the booty of the idols, slain with the snout of a swordfish.

In the ninth month of *Tlazochimaco* the people sought the mountain dahlia, the tigridia, the petals of the nymphæ, a Sierra ruffian magnolia, and the carnal plumeria. The young Aztec warriors wore long hair and were continent while the dotard Nestor and senile Menelaus drank wine, and great boasts wrinkled their toothless mouths and stomachs as they sat on the ground beneath the fires of *Popocatepetl*, remembering when they were volcanoes.

Chicomecoatl was the goddess of food and beverages, and *Centeotl* counseled physicians and midwives, and held a shield in one hand and a broom in the other. *Texacatlipoca* strode the heavens and earth and hell and sowed hatred and wars between men and nations. *Quetzalcoatl*, the deity of trade at *Cholula*, had a comb of warts, and stuck out his tongue. There were parturition, pest, abortion, plague and palsy idols. These deities give us clear knowledge of the people, whether they be despotic, stupid, grum, or vegetarian, and to what extent skulduggery and falsehood are venerated. There were trade gods; *Chalchiuhtily cue*, goddess of water, had power over seas and rivers, and her devotees were those who sold goods from their canoes, or those who vended fruits and herbs in big earthen jars in the market place. In Attica the market was a hallowed place; Socrates,

84

Crates, and Zeno often went to the Agora where frankincense, poppy seeds, and mules were sold, and where the bones of Hesiod the poet were buried.

The Nahuas also had a goddess *Ciuacoatl*, a harpy Hecate who gave men misery and toil, the hoe and the tump-line, which are the thorns and the thistles into which Adam was cast. *Ciuacoatl* is a wise work figure, for men must toil, or die of satiety.

These remnants of Tartary knew the old Asian sins of Ham, and they set aside hermaphrodites which are like the apples of the Dead Sea whose core contained the clinkers of Sodom. The Pueblo Indians observed similar rites, and the Zuñis had androgynous deities. Indian women of Paraguay wore an image of the pudendum as an amulet. Stone and terra cotta effigies of Priapus were found in ancient graves in Peru and at Tabasco. Ancient phallic pillars stood in the Valley of Mexico, but they were the dead ruins of the *Tolteca* who came before the fierce *Chichimecas*. When the soldiers of Cortes came to *Panuco* they saw the Phallus in bas-relief on the walls of old temples. Men build edifices to Priapus which is no better than offering incense or a barren ewe to a disease. Such phallic stone obelisks are still to be seen in the lower Mississippi Valley and in Tabasco. Some of the Indian rites and customs of Eros who guards pulse and corn are saner testimonials of man's unquenchable sottishness.

*   *   *   *   *

The Indian was a cunning mime. The warriors of *Tlatelulco*, desiring to overcome the Mexicans, hid in the reeds, and simulated the shapes and noises of ravens, geese, and frogs. The Fuegians, who have no alphabet, can reproduce the gait of one of their tribe with more skill than Homer was able to limn Agamemnon or Nestor.

The Nahuatl words are of volcanic origin, and the consonants as rough as the peaks of *Tlaloc*, and rarely voweled. The Songs of Solomon to the Shulamite are soft water vowels, and the vanity thereof is the cry of the turtledoves.

The materials of the Indian manuscripts show remarkable culture; the Aztecan papyrus was of the fabric of the *Agave* whose *maguey* leaves were employed as thatch for the roofs of the houses and as food and drink. The ancient Mexican also made rush seats out of the same reed with which he wrote.

The numeral seven was as holy to the Aztec as it is in the *Kabala*; could they have borrowed their marriage ceremony from the Chassidic sect? The Indian bride, like a mystic daughter of Israel, circled the groom seven times, her veil tied to his tunic.

Privy members of the Aztec children were cut, a practice similar to Jewish circumcision. The poor Indian brought quails to the demigods; in ancient Judea humble people brought a pair of turtledoves to the altar. Without a regard for penury man is a vile Plutus.

Penance was commonly observed, and though Sahagun tells us that only the old men and women confessed their vices, this shows unusual discernment; for the young there are the rigors and the sins, but for the aged there is confession and the waiting for death.

Except on the rarest occasions, only the old men and women, those who were heavy with desolation, and required wine or pulque to make them merry, were permitted to drink. This merciful license is allowed the aged as is shown in *Proverbs*.

It is possible that what all men learn was known of old, and this is a miserable thought as each one would like to assume that he is better or knows more than Cain or Lamech or Manco Capac. The theogony of Hesiod is puerile to them who are certain they are not. But nobody is wise all the time, and only man, himself, could make such a boastful remark.

IX

THE INCA was a Theban of the Andes; the first Inca came out of a crag at *Paucartampu*. The peaks of mountains were his *huacas* or idols; he venerated the Sierras and the Punas and his grief was dry. Rocks are the herbals of sun races. Medusa is less of a marvel than the hot fountain in the *Guancauilca* in Peru, which, as it pours forth, turns into pebbles. Stones are the remedies for the grieving mind and the flesh which are water and grass. Grass and rivers are the pleasures of men which pass away, but the ravines and hills mineral the will. The Egyptian embalmers at Heliopolis turned the head of the deceased away from the River Nile. The *Chotas* of Mexico worship the dawn and stones; *Tohil*, the god who gave the *Quiché Maya* fire by shaking his sandals, was of obsidian origin. The primal gods sprang up from an aerolite that had fallen from the skies.

The great cities were built on the verteber of the *Cordilleras*; the Andes travel to Chile, and on the route to that country are the mountains of *Pariacaca* where the air congeals the veins and makes sorrow flow like granite. These mountains have the same effect upon the mind as the climate of Quito where the Indians fell into a metaphysical melancholia and slew themselves; the pure air of Quito is the fire of philosophy, and will breed Gymnosophists. The swans, by which the ancients meant priests and prophets, will appear in this land; men delight in such purity for it is best to die by philosophy; in the cave of Apollo there is a pool whose waters make men prophetic, though it shortens their lives.

On the days of the Inca's festivals the *huacas* were removed from the temples, and the mummies who had been lords and queens were washed in the baths which they had used, and then carried in litters to the holy city of Cuzco. Here they gave *chichá*, boiled maize, to the embalmed ones. They also offered coneys, tallow, coca and raiment to the *huacas*.

When the demons were brought out for adoration the Inca abstained from salt; maids were chosen to carry the *chichá* in golden vases to the House of the Sun and the Thunder. During one of the festivals of the *Quiché Maya* a priest was sent to the woods to garner dew from leaves which had never been touched by woman.

The Inca banished the deformed from holy places save on certain feasts; the blind, the one-handed could not enter the temple of Jerusalem. A dwarf excites the perverse lusts; and a gnome from Punt was of more value to a Pharaoh than balsam or gold from Nubia. The sacrificial animal of the Inca and the Israelite was without defect; the Essene went in a white stole, and the Inca damsel wore golden shoes made of the fibers of the aloe tree.

Counting was held to be base by the Inca, and arithmetic, unless it is related to the pulsations of the sea, the moon, the setting of the Pleiads, or the harvest, is another word for avarice. They had unusual esteem for sages, or philosophers whom they called *Amatuas*, though the Inca had no alphabet. Letters is more of a fox than the tongue. The Aztec codices were the serpents we call art.

One who told falsehoods was punished by death; the slothful were mocked, and he who fell behind in his duties to the *huacas* had to carry toads fashioned out of salt. Those who kept their vows, and cast the ashes of Indian sheep, or the *guanacos*, and the sacred cloth into the river were allowed to bear lances and falcons wrought of salt. Inca morals are but the stems and boughs of Inca rituals. It is asserted that a female *huaca* having fornicated with a man was turned into a stone.

Great people seldom trust themselves, there is so little of man, either his arm, his hand, or his foot that arouses confidence. Either the elbow is craven, the fingers are ten perjurers, or the foot awakens licentious thoughts. When Amen-Rā, the sun-god, prevailed among the Egyptians, Pharaoh put the figure of Truth around his neck before judging the malefactor, nor could he say what penalty any fault was worth until the priests of Heliopolis consulted the papyri upon which the laws were written.

The first ancestor of the Inca is Manco Capac, child of the Sun, born of a rock which is more constant than the human heart. Manco Capac had three brothers of a more unstable nature, one called Ayar Cachi, signifying salt, the second, Ayai Vohu, a pepper, and the third Ayan Sanca, who is mirth and contentment.

Human appetite grows like the craw of Tantalus; once fed with salt or pepper for which the sensual nations sought a new route to *Cipango*, it ranges the world for more seasoned deliriums and voluptuous traumas. When man starves his gullet, he is entitled to the appellation Cato instead of his usual surname, cormorant.

Manco Capac founded the sacred city of Cuzco, and the maize and pulse raised there were priestly plants; an Inca seeing a pilgrim from Cuzco lowered his eyes or retired to one of his chambers.

Manco Capac taught the Inca to sow maize, for husbandry tames the passions. The Inca regarded savage or fallow ground as having a hardened heart. He instructed the Inca parents to press the heads of their infants until they were flat and stupid, for he thought that otherwise they would have round, virile craniums, and be insolent. The fathers of unruly children were severely punished. Youths at seventeen were given white breeches as a sign of their virtue and warrior strength. They retired to the hills, near Cuzco, to fast, and their fathers flogged them to remind them of their oaths and the valor of their ancestors.

He established houses for virgins who baked bread and wove the robes for the Sun; but no vestal or woman was permitted to enter the temple of the Sun. Manco Capac told the Inca that when girls combed and plaited their hair they were women. Not all work was equal. Some virgins were chosen to be porters; Yupanqui, a descendant of Manco Capac, ordered deformed and idiotic persons to be trained as weavers.

Manco Capac set the falcon, the hummingbird, snake, fox

and toad in the hills. The boldest warrior is a falcon, the cunning one is a fox and a serpent, and the sluggard is a toad. Whatever the Inca learned from the falcon and the hummingbird was of small value, for the vices of the serpent, the fox, and the toad are much dearer to him.

Manco Capac told them of *Pachacamac*. Pacha is the Universe, and Camac is the Quickener. This name was as sacred as *Elohim*, and was not to be uttered by a pious Inca except when meditating or preparing to die. Until Manco Capac was old he was a philosopher. But when he was senile, he endeavored to find out who *Pachacamac* is, which is beyond the understanding of men. He prayed to the imageless Person, offering up an immaculate Indian lamb, hoping for some sign or word. The oval plate in the temple representing *Pachacamac* is an absolute blank. Unable to exact an answer from the Universe, he slew his son as a sacrificial gift, and so he became the Cain of the Incas.

Were it not that man is irrational either in the beginning or at the close of his life, Manco Capac would have been a god. His good principles confound men, his bad ones startle the puma.

A wise man may write a marvelous tragedy, and bray no less than the asinine penguin. In many ways he is less than Leviathan or Behemoth. Man is the most unstable brute, and knows less about himself than the widgeon, the fox or the seal.

X

FRANCISCO HERNANDES DE CORDOBA and his men arrived at the Bay of Campeche, where they went ashore on Lazarus Sunday. Twenty Spaniards were killed, fifty wounded and those taken by the Mayans were sacrificed to their idols. With thirty-three holes in his body Cordoba returned to Cuba. What he told of the realm of Yucatan inflamed Hernando Cortes who left Cuba with a fleet of ships and men, his own pinnace bearing a banner honoring Our Lady.

Those who came to America seeking a new water route to Cathay found the remnant sons of Ham. All races are a confusion of first peoples, of Lamech, Japhet, Ham and Cush; the gross Cyclopes are said to be the progeny of Cush, the

Egyptian pyramid builders, and his descendants, the Toltecs, architects of the temples at Cholula.

The races in the Plains of Shinar, in the Valley of Mesopotamia, and in Hellas have common origins; Greece was populated by the sons of Javan, and the Lacedaemonians acknowledge that they were of the same family as the Caphtorim of Palestine; genealogy is a vast myth; the record of man, apart from legend, is stepmother history.

The Tartarian Chan was Ham who was given Asia as his portion. The children of Ham wept for their forefathers; they had forgotten the wain and the wheel; and the elephant, the unicorn, and the horse had long since disappeared; instead of the buffalo that grazed in the pastures of Cathay, the North American Indian hunted, but did not yoke the bison. The bison is the woolly Indian buffalo, his cattle were deer, the hare and mute dogs. There were cow and wool trees in the New World, but no heifer or sheep, and no Joseph to dream of lean or fat kine.

The *Quiché Maya* had a jaguar *Genesis*, and they had an old Semitic word, Balam, meaning soothsayer; like the profane Balaam, in the *Old Testament*, this Balam was the jaguar priest.

Quiché is forest, for they were a tree people, longing to roof and bed their wives; and the title of their sacred book, made of tree bark, is *Popol Vuh*, which are *Quiché* words for together, or common house. Their knowledge of the first days of the earth came from the coyote, the owl and vampire bat; the ant told *Quetzalcoatl* where to find the corn seeds.

The *Quiché Maya* say that primeval man was shaped out of mud; Adam in Hebrew is virgin red clay. There are North American Indians who suppose that when the world was a circle of water, a crawfish brought up mud from the sea bottom. The Adam of the *Quiché* was unable to move his head, and his face fell to one side, and he could not look behind, which is the tragedy of the inhabitants of the New World. He had no mind, which is nothing else but turning one's eyes toward the past. These creatures were destroyed and were followed by figures of wood that peopled the earth; they were dry of cheek, and their feet and hands were stupid, and they had four parched legs. The women were fashioned out of river rushes, but nobody thought, and the men and women were wood, osier, and soulless legs and hands. They were drowned in the Deluge, or were devoured by eagles, or sparrowhawks, their nerves broken by bats, and their bones hewn to pieces by jaguars. Owls were their enemies, and so was pride which they called *Hunahpu*, the arrogant *Quiché* Nimrod, and the same *Quiché* word stands for fragrant flower.

Zipacna took their mountains to the sea where there were crabs to eat, and *Cabracan* was their earthquake giant. The Mayan, or his brother, the *Yaqui*, or Mexican, were flower priests who flensed human skulls; fennel, sage, and the odors of the delicate *tixzula* did not cure their murdering blood. A soldier of Cortes said that he counted a hundred thousand skulls on the racks in the Mayan temples.

The calendar of the Mayans and Aztecs was more accurate than the Julian year; the Inca set up weather towers on summits, and the Mayans erected square pillars, or sacred *Katuns*, every twenty years. On these *Katuns* they kept many of the memorials of their forefathers; the Colchians had pillars on which they represented the continents of the world and Ocean. One of the earliest symbols for Zeus was a pyramid, the shape of fire. Prometheus, who is fire, was a castaway on Mount Caucasus hard by Colchis.

The Aztec and the Mayan had much reverence for the day and the month; every day is an Angel bringing men fortune or hardship, either of which requires the most austere discipline to endure. The *Quiché Maya* month of *Queb* is a deer and also the ear of green corn; *Tzizil Lakam* is the eleventh month when the sprouts show themselves, and desire pulls up the blood, and the maiden's petticoats. *Tziquin Kib* gathers the birds and their song, and *Cakam* is the time for red clouds. *Huahpu* is hunger, the wise Buddha of the covetous stomach.

There were eighteen months in the Mayan year, and a devil for each who received copal or bread and calabash seeds. They showed their adoration for the month *Muluc* by bringing to its image fifty-three grains of ground maize and copal. In the month they called *Mol*, the artisans gathered cedar out of which they carved the deities. At this time they fasted and had no commerce with women. There was a month called *Nabey Man*, signifying the first old man or evil omen, for where there is no strength there is no hope of good chance or a wise fate, for neither Zeus nor Aphrodite nor Pallas Athene pays any heed to the weak.

* * * * *

Three months are given to white flowers; they hold that there are five barren days, which are very few, had they not dropsical demons, or did they not cringe before *Tatan bak* and *Tatan Holom*, one the father of bones, and the other of skulls. They have a strong awe of death and rot; their word, *Cayala*, means the yellow ears of corn, which is their principal food, but *Cay* is the putrid matter in water from which maize first sprang.

The names they give their days are not the Indian crater words, but are China or Tibetan travelers; *Tob* is rain or tempest, and *Jmox* is fish, *Cat* is a weir for a lizard, or an iguana whose meat they relish. There was the cacique *Nachen Can; Can,* like *Atl,* or *Ch'en,* Indian months, are Tartary words. The *Quiché Maya* months have the same Asian origin, and this is old world understanding. They brought their month and day names from the China mainland, carrying them in their heads, as they did their gods, or *Bacabs,* upon their backs.

Many of the idols of the Mayans are naked figures of men whose genitals are covered by long fillets. Though these Indians regarded human flesh as the most palatable venison they hated thieves; their houses had no doors, which is very wise, since men usually take what is hidden from them. It was very costly to filch a Mayan maidenhead, for they seized the malefactor and drew out his intestines through the navel. For the seduction of another's wife, they stoned the adulterer to death. They elected the most beautiful women to pour water or wine from the calabash, which they did turning away from the men as they served them.

The *Quiché Maya* have a barbaric Virgin Mary, *Xquic,* Little Blood, whose father is *Cuchumaquic,* the Blood-Gatherer. Their hero is *Hhun-Hunahpu* who is a skull in the Calabash tree. Whoever partook of the fruit of this heathen Tree of Life ate a human head. *Xquic* had a great pining to have one of these gourds, and reaching for the fruit a few drops of tree spittle fell from the fruited skull upon her and she conceived. She is the mother of the Aztec god of war, *Huitzilopochtli.*

At *Chiapas* there is the dragon tree which bleeds; the tree of Cochineal sheds those tears of gore which satisfy men no less than Patagonian ore. The tree is an Indian god, and each locality is his kindred. He is not alone in the forests, among

97

the rocks, or in the thistles, and the Mayan knew little of that fever cankering all men, being apart. Suffering together is the lesser pang, and the Mexican and the Mayan tell how the tribes, after they had left Panuco, wandered in the woods together, having lost the sacred seeds *Quetzalcoatl* gave them.

The natives of Yucatan were as vulnerable to odors as the vine which is queasy when it is near the cabbage or the radish. Whether people smell good or not is the reason for considering them virtuous though Lazarus and Doctor Samuel Johnson stank. Chastity, too, is what the nose thinks is savory; the Indians honored the virgin-cloth, but did not think a widow worth a wedding. When an Indian desired to marry a widow, he went to her house, and if she gave him food they were man and wife. The Mayan traveler took with him incense and a small brazier in which to burn it, and he paid homage to the *Bacabs* of the Four Directions by perfuming the stones which stood for them.

They filled the mouth of the dead with maize, and after sawing the hinder part of the cranium stuffed it with some kind of mumia, or bitumen, as the ancient Egyptians did. They abhorred theft, homicide, and liars; as they used cacao for money and stones for counters, and many held their lands in common, there was little cause to steal. The European lied to increase his fate; the Indian only told falsehoods to protect his earth.

The Indian mother had the copious paps of the Ephesian Diana, because she ground maize without tying up her breasts, and she often gave her milk to a deer or a dog. Indian women baked the cassava bread or washed their clothes in the rivers with a soap made of the ashes of the elm, but there are few chronicles of their amorous inclinations. In North America the Indian woman rises from her sleep, when the moon has risen, and dances naked around the maize she has sown. Among the natives of Brazil a man spoke to a woman with his back turned towards her, which is often more sensible than facing her which he cannot do without showing her his genital organs. The Indian woman, wearing a cloth that dropped no farther than her navel, is said to have been as modest.

The Caciques at *Tlaxcala* sent Cortes gold and silver, feathers, raiment, soles for sandals, and four Indian crones, which greatly displeased his soldiers. A fat *curaca* presented his ugly niece to Cortes, and as he knew how to smile as well as Iago, he put on a joyful face. Pedro de Alvarado, who ravished Yucatan and Guatemala for Hernando Cortes, hung one Indian damsel and a wife on a tree because he said their beauty would make the Spaniards discontented. When the *Quiché Maya* declared war upon Alvarado they crucified a virgin puppy and a woman in a ravine.

XI

THE HOT LANDS of America grow prodigies similar to the tale of the *Camucuiara* who are said to have paps that nuzzle their knees, and which they bind around their waists when they run or hunt. The stories about unipeds, people with horse's feet and dog's heads, are Hesiodic fable and zoology. Magellan saw Patagonians who were eight feet tall, though Darwin assures us they were no more than six.

Brazil is a Canaan in the morning, but a scorpion and a spider by midday. One voyager has observed the climate flows with poison. There is scarce a stone from the sea coast by *Pernambuco* to the Province of the Holy Ghost, and men are impatient and gross infidels without rocks or Sierras.

Energy is a mighty god, and the Indian word for the great, brute waters is *Parana;* there is the bursting flood, the *Paranambuco.* But the rivers of Brazil are angels sown with dragon's teeth.

The most infamous eaters of human flesh are the humid water nations of the Americas. They dwell in the *Sertãos* of Brazil or people the gloomy lake regions. They are fierce hunters greedy for incense and flowers; the falcon is a bird of rapine whose breakfast is the hummingbird which dotes on the honey of flowers. Their animals are hot and loathly, either giving off the evil odor of the fox, or the fragrance of the musk snake. Their food is a galling fillip to the stomach and the soul; Indian pepper is called *Carib*, a cannibal spice which kindles lusts; they eat battle bread made from the savage, spinous yucca; the *mandioca* root provides them with another kind of bread, although the juice is fatal.

The face of these natives is homogeneous, lacking the havoc and the rueful lines which are the work of the intellect. The nose, though Caucasian, which has the long, aquiline look of a Euripides or a Solon, is a mummer of thought. The Indian seldom balds, and many men would become savages solely to be as hairy as the bear or the pard.

These natives are raw patriarchs; the Indian Abraham cuts the navel string with his teeth, which gives him the right to rule his children. There is no patricide by the River of January, for when a child is peevish or unpleasant, the father lashes him; they have enough tenderness for their children to protect them from growing up to be gourmets or indolent. The Inca despise gluttony, giving the infant the breast to suck three times a day, no matter how much he cries for more of his mother's teats. The natives of Brazil beat their children with thistles to harden them sufficiently to dwell in the woods. Some of the aboriginals never chastise their children, who, after they have reached puberty, are as irascible as the fly.

The Brazil native governs his wife, seldom quarreling with her, and when he hates her he waits until he is drunk to strike her so that he can blame the wine for his act. He shows a marvelous regard for women, permitting only withered crones or virgins to prepare his wine; the maids and hags take the *mandioca* root into their mouths, and after champing it between their teeth spew the juice into a calabash.

There are as many tribes in Brazil as there are rivers, and their names have been catalogued as the descendants of Cush, Ham and Japhet are, and they eat men. A brave Indian of Brazil, about to be devoured by his captors, said it was better to be the venison of man than to die and stink and be a meal for worms. There are seventy-six nations of the *Tapuyas* who are anthropophagous; their enemies are the *Tapuxerig* who call themselves their foes so that they can devour their corn fields without feeling unjust.

Most of the Indians in these regions were cannibals; the tribes, as well as the waters of this land, are tributaries of one another as Put and Canaan are the sons of Ham. The natives living between the upper *Orinoco, Rio Negro,* the *Jnirida,* and the *Jupura* devoured human flesh. For the lack of cattle they ate men; there was no pastoral life, and the natives of the *Orinoco* traveled with the seeds of corn, squash, beans, melons. In the place of poultry the timorous inhabitants of the Indies who brought calabashes, plantains, cassavas, and tears to Cristóbal Colon, fed upon the macaw whose skin is black and tough. Bears that frequented the shores of the *Temi* were considered savory table meat by the

Indian. The *Guahibos* fed on scolopendras and worms rather than sow cassava or maize. The horse in America became a nomad on the *llanos* and would have been a cannibal Indian or one of the steeds of Diomedes who were said to care for human flesh.

The *Tapoyes* inhabit the coast, and their name in the Indian language means a wild man, a word held in exceptional derision among the cannibals of Brazil. The *Waytaquazes* at *Cape Frio* are very fierce and can take a huge dogfish by the tail and haul it ashore. The *Wayannases* have their habitation south of the River of January; they are notorious poltroons, and their daintiest victual is man. The *Petivares* are not so barbaric; they make a hole in their lips with the horn of a roebuck; they are naked and range northern Brazil from *Baya* to the *Rio Grande,* and they eat everybody.

Cannibalism was the sin of the Anakim, the giants who were the progenitors of Cyclops. This unnatural gluttony was practiced by the Laestrygones who worshipped snakes. The American savage consumed people as well as toads, serpents, crocodiles, and they named their great waters after them. The Sirens beckoned the mariners to the coasts of Italy where they were shipwrecked and became the meal of the Lamii.

After passing the River of *Paraeyva,* one comes to the country of the *Molopaques,* who cover their secret parts, and have much gold which they do not care for and use on their fishing lines in the River of *Para.* Their women are very modest, and never laugh; wit, the parent of malice and of letters, is not one of the traits of primitive nations. The *Motayas* come dancing and singing to meet strangers, bringing them the *mandioca* root and pepper as gifts. They abhor the *Tamoyes* and devour them whenever possible. The women are exceedingly hospitable, and as soon as a guest arrives, they weep bitterly over him and caress his shoulders and knees, a custom that arouses very envious feelings in occidental nations.

These savages have a houseless hardihood; the *Guaitica* do not inhabit their huts except when they go to bed. The Indians of the *Orinoco* and of the *Atures*, abounding in granite, pay little heed to doors, and have no keys of which creeds and rosaries are made; the *Piaroas* that live near the little *Catanaiapo* wear the teeth of the peccary around their necks. Some of the tribes do not sup on human flesh; the *Cumpache* are content to cut off the heads of people who trouble them. The *Carayas*, who occupy the banks of the Upper Saint Antonio, kill defenseless foreigners, but barter courteously with those who have weapons. The climate produces too many rivers; the heat engenders the dwarfish *Tarape*, and those who call themselves the *Nonea* and who have immense faces which can do little else but gawk. The *Tupinaquin* are a revengeful brood; they lie with all women, or as many as they have the strength for, and are now reported to be Christians. Cannibals are not interested in rapine or the occidental disease called love, and do not find it essential to practice furtive polygamy, as a woman can be had for a knife or a hatchet.

Sancta Cruz is the Christian appellation of this country whose rivers and bays bear the names of apostles and Saint Francis, the sainted pauper. Brazil is a red wood and a tree of trade; cacao grains were Indian money; in Guiana the inhabitants used small snails for currency. Greed diminishes the virgin energies, and man is as weak as grass. Metals also sorrow; Galen and Monardes write that iron suffers a grievous disease which can be cured by anointing it with the marrow of a deer.

The trees of Brazil know more than Aesculapius or Hippocrates; the bark of the *Acaiu* tree is a remedy for sores and imposthumes. This tree distills a gum that is good to paint with; worms provided the Mayans with some of their pigments which artists use as though they were drunkards. It was long ago remarked, and, alas, since forgot, that painting is a book for fools who cannot read.

The *Ombu* is a water trunk more precious to travelers than pride; the *Cabueriba* is esteemed for that balm wearied Jeremiah sought in Gilead; wounded animals rub themselves on this bark until the liquor pours forth upon their hurts. The *Jgcigca* gives the sweet-smelling mastic which takes the place of incense. There is a species of Brazil peach good for the pox; the flower of the *Caaroba* is reported to be as fine a medicine as China Wood for those who are mocked by Venus. In the land of the macaw Adam's tree is known as the *Pacoba*, the leaves of which cool grief and the ague. The *Moriche* palm is a water tree, growing about the *Guayaval* and the *Piritu*; this is the tree of raiment, and wine and flour of the *Guaraunos* who say the serpents give them moisture which the forests require. The palm tree of the Pampas could not afford enough shade for a melancholy Saul or a parched Jonah. The milk of the pawpaw is nutritious, but it does not take the place of the heifers of the Amaleks or the paps of Diana. The *Tamanac* believe that after the flood South America was repeopled by the seeds of the *Mauritia* palm tree from which they sprang. The priests at Hermopolis had the branches of palms in their sandals and were as wise as the Chaldeans. In Yucatan the giant *Ceiba* is regarded as the Tree of Life, but no one has ever eaten of this wood.

The cocoa tree is the olive of South America, but it thrives upon salt water which kills men or drives them mad. Beyond the cataracts of *Ature* and *Maypure* are cocoa groves, but these regions are plagued with worms, ants, insects, and cannot assuage the weariness of the Psalmist. Trees are wanderers too, and they suffer from the worm, the wart, and acquire novel or deranged habits in strange climes; the *mamee-apple*, the plantain, and the alligator pear thrive upon sea water, and can be said to be original but perverse flora.

Wild trees are the hardiest, but they produce no fruit; the palms of the *Mauritias* of South America furnished the Indian with threads for hammocks and beverages rather than legends; Euripides writes that Latona gave birth to Apollo and Diana beneath a palm tree, and Homer tells us that Phoenix, one of the horses of Diomedes, was the color of a palm.

XII

THE HOT LANDS of America are a snake fable. When Cortes arrived on the shore of *Chalchicuecan* in 1519, there was not one domestic animal in *Terra Firma;* the elephants had long since vanished, and only extinct fossils of the horse have been found.

There was no shepherd, no Virgil or Propertius to lament the feral peccary, tapir, armadillo, condor, or guanaco. Jacques Cartier had called the New World *Terra damnata.*

Man is the most vain of all the animals in the earth, though in most respects he is no better than a polypus, which also has a mouth, intestines, and organs. Man is more superstitious and his manners are more irregular than these creatures, and his malice is more essential to him. Aristotle has said that animals only die at neap tide, but men perish wantonly in all months and seasons.

Wild ground produces the worst feeders; putrid whale or seal blubber is a great delicacy for the Fuegian, whereas in the central part of *Tierra del Fuego* hummingbirds drink the pith of flowers, and parrots rejoice in the seeds of Winter's Bark. The civet cat of Brazil is a remarkable teacher; its diet is honey, but none is touched until the young and the senile cat is called to join in the meal. The armadillo tastes like the flesh of the hen and has the muzzle of a sucking pig; wallets are made of the skin of this barbed horse, which were better for mankind were they sieves. The peccary is the hog of the woods; the tapir pastures only at night, abhorring the sun, and is as perverse a prodigy of the New World as the Indian.

The sloth bellies the ground as it goes, but it is as delicate a feeder as the ancient Essene, starving to death without fig leaves. The *jacuacini* are wallowing brutes, slubbered with sleep, who eat sea crabs and browse among the sugar canes. The *jagoarucu* are Brazilian dogs with the teeth of eagles who dote on fruit. The *tapati* are coneys who bark, and the *pacai* are feral pigs that swim in the Saint Francis. The *macucagua* is a very small bird; when it sings it is an omen of spring rains, but when it eats it shows the crop of Cerberus.

The lizard adorns the sterile lava isles in the Pacific, and this primal creature is herbivorous and without malice, for he is as content with sea weed as Diogenes was with a peck of lupines. The Galapagos tortoise, the finch and the lizard eat the cactus together as brothers.

The condor, a carrion feeder, is a social bird that lives in pairs, and in parts of South America these garbage-eaters roost together with others of their kind in trees. It is said of the *Polyborus Chimango* that when he is in a passion he plucks up the grass to satisfy his rage, but this is a feathered cenobite, and though men go into the wilderness to quell their spleen, few come out of the forest with a timorous mien or spirit. The ostrich in Northern Patagonia lives on roots and grass and prefers to be apart from others. When man is separated from companions he is a swinish eater, without domestic affections, dwelling meanly in deserts or caverns, and without fables to ease his bile or warm his bowels for others.

The *anima* is a rapacious bird, and the Indians say that the horn on its comb or beak is a remedy for people whose words fall out of their mouths too early or late. Other birds of prey are the falcon, merlin, eagle, and the goshawk. The fishermen of Galilee were no gentler than this predatory fowl until it had knowledge of men.

* * * * *

Nature riots in the hot lands of the New World, and surfeit begets monsters and griffins Homer dare not fable. A serpent has two mouths, one in its tail. Another has the skin of the prickly pear.

There is a great ape whose whiskers sprout in the lower chap, and wherever he goes he is accompanied by a wean. When this large, hairy Esau cries out, foam gathers on his beard which the young one wipes away. The monkeys that inhabit the woods and the banks of the *Apure* or the *Rio Negro* cleave to the parents as Ruth did to Naomi. They cling to the backs of their mothers which have been killed by arrows or darts, and must be torn from them. They fear very much to be hurt, and if they perceive any danger, their eyes fill with the waters of Heshbon.

Brazil, the land of the popinjays, christened *Sancta Cruz*, has the energy of the serpent. The Indian, when bitten by a venomous reptile, drank from the horn of the unicorn, known as snake wood. When an Indian woman is barren she is struck on the hips with a snake. On the holy days of the Aztecs the virgins wear vines of maize and the bones of vipers. Neither the fig nor the cocoa tree has subdued them. The poison of the *Jararaca* flows from a tooth like saffron water. The animals confound the senses as though the species of one had coupled with those of another.

Men are more bizarre than animals. They are as jealous as the male crocodiles in the coupling season. The guanaco, before domesticated by man, pays little heed to the female, but after he has lived in association with human beings, he bites any one who approaches the dam in his corral. The guanaco has ridiculous passions and a slavish noddle; he prances before his assassin, making silly, amorous capers; these beasts march in platoons to the salinas, for salt water refreshes their throats. But no ancient barrow or cenotaph is more noble than the dying guanaco, who crawls to the marge of a river to leave his bones by the waters. His end is more important than his life. We would be indifferent to human fate were it not that man dies.

Men take their habits from animals, and they lose their symbolic life apart from them. They are also as vehement as the reptiles in the earth they have not cured. Man is without calm until he has sown his follies in the matrix of Tamar, and he is as mournful afterwards as the swan who sings his own dirge. The mastic, the nutmegs, and cloves for which he had ploughed all seas are chaff in his head and his one cry is for a crypt, an epitaph, the funeral worms.

Man is the tragic animal and is as waspish as the *yapu* bird, who has a strong odor when he frets. He makes many books which are intolerable scorpions, which, in Brazil are said to sleep in men's boots, and to be ecstatic when lying in the libraries.

The legends of a continent without household animals, timorous streams, and social birds, except the macaw and parrot bred in the swamps of the *Sertão*, are battle Kabala of creation. It is told that after the Deluge the coyote planted the feathers of the various birds from which sprang up all the tribes of men.

XIII

THE FOUR RIVERS of Paradise water all wisdom; the Pison flows about Havilah, near the mouth of the Indus; the Gihon is the Nile, the Tigris is an Assyrian arrow, and the Euphrates is called Perath in *Genesis*; their children are the Mississippi, tumulus of De Soto, and the five tribal inland seas of the Iroquois and the Hurons. There is the Colorado, the *Rio Palmas*, or the Rio Grande, the Missouri, and these are our heads, loins, and dorsal muscles, still Indian fetch, and to be canonized and resettled. The River of January is the body of Poseidon which covers more than fourteen leagues of the land of Brazil. The *Orinoco* and the *Meta* are the beds of the crocodile, the eels or gymnotus; the *Rio Guarico* falls into the *Apure,* and beyond the *Meta* and the *Arauca* is *El Dorado.* These waters are no laughing nymphs, and Michael, the Archangel, who saw Adam by the Jordan, had not blessed the *Rio Negro* or the furies of the *Amazon.*

There are no apocalyptic waters in *Terra Firma,* and we know of no Daniel who stood on the banks of Ulai, or of a Baruch weeping over the captivity of Jerusalem upon the River Gel. The continent is still a massive valley of Jehosaphat, and whether it contains the bones of an Isaiah, or if the prophets be those mastodons which the moon melted when the children of Noah divided the earth, is unknown. The rivers of the New Hemisphere belong to the first six days of creation; the cosmographer quarries every stream and current; for water is the seer of dream, which was the map in the heads of Cartier, Cabot and Cabral.

America is battle earth and its rivers are great water brutes; the *Rio Negro,* the *Parana, Da Prata* are unsocial waters, the navel strings of Ocean. Sea calves and whales swim in the bays and at the mouths of the rivers where the bivalves sing.

The River of Toads is hard by the River of Saint Francis, and there is another marvelous stream called Saint Michael. The Angel Uriel stands guard over Cocytus and Phlegethon in Tartarus, but it takes a long time for men to learn how to weep by the marges of rivers.

*　*　*　*　*

The guitar strings, made of the muscles of a boa or from the intestines of the *alouate* monkey, did not provide the songs of the swans that made Apollo melancholy. When rivers age, and grow small and mild, Daniel, Artemis and Pan frequent their banks. Water in its dotage is the cause of a psalm or a poem, for Neptune, Poseidon, and Proteus, who

113

are water, are old men, and the swan's most poignant song is known as his senilia, and the River Strymon was his ancient home.

Our annals are weak, and we know not our rivers; we cannot understand today which is Father Rā, the Egyptian sun, until we gather up yesterday, who is Osiris. These rivers are immense legends and would cure us of many ills, did we know them, for all nature is our corpus, and once we relinquish a part of the earth, we lose, in some way, the use of our hands, feet, loins, and spirit.

The Florida current was a seer, as great a navigator as Cristóbal Colon or Magellan or Drake; the gulf, the warm channel in the Sea of Darkness, was an intimation of a passage to Japan; there had been hints of the existence of a world beyond the Pillars; the trunk of a *Cedrela odorata* was found at Santa Cruz near Teneriffe; two red-skinned corpses had been washed ashore at the Azores; the beaches of Gomera were strewn with fruits from the Antilles; storms had driven Esquimaux, in canoes of wolves' skins, to the Orkneys. Nature divulges its secrets, but man is slow to fathom them. The tortoise, coming from the waters of Cuba, and found on the coasts of Scotland, was a quicker cosmographer than man.

Vulcan, known to the ancients as a navigator, had revealed none of his knowledge to the Indian who remained in the Americas; only the corpses, some bamboo trees from Brazil, cane, and the trunks of the *Ceiba,* journeyed to Europe, and none, except *Quetzalcoatl,* and his retinue, left the land of Dido or shipped out from Tyre, or Sidon, to thresh a sea for an American fate.

The River Achelous heaped up the mud for the Echinades islands, and Delos was a gift of the seas; Memphis was the bodies of Thetis and Neptune which are ancient sea water, but the *Orinoco*, the *Uruguay*, and the *Amazon* are as old as Deluge. The coffer of the *Orinoco* is wrought of granite. Stone and water shape the character of peoples. Rocks and rapids winter the blood and give a grum honesty to the tribes. The lecherous crocodile abhors the cataracts.

The *Orinoco* is the bed of the emu and the manatee, whose fat was burnt as oil in the lamps in the churches. The manatee is marine table pork for the Indians of Brazil; born in salt estuaries, the manatee goes to fresh water to drink and feeds on the leaves of the mangrove tree. This animal has the flavor of an ox, and its intestines are laden with grass. When there is a dearth of this mammiferous animal, or when he goes to other fresh-water seas, the *Ottomac* eats earth. The emu is a big river sheep. There is a fish called the caribe whose belly is a serrated saw, and can cut a crocodile to pieces, which is also the proper appellation of these rivers that would be the visage of God were they not voracious.

Four watery Nimrods flow over the back of the *Cordilleras*, and they are the *Meta*, the *Guaviare*, the *Caqueta*, and the *Putumayo*. Rivers make men contemplative and slake the soul. Large, feral waters confound the races of the earth. New ground is too original for men, and the animals are paradoxes. Wild man goes to the marshes where the crocodiles swarm. The white heron treads upon the scaly back of the sleeping reptile; the saurians and the jaguars show diverse habits in various great streams.

Carved emeralds have been found in Quito, and some fix *El Dorado* on the declivities of the Andes; rivers of gold rise in this mountain. The mountains of *Encaramada* and the ranges of the *Mato* were the matrix of the *Rio Asiveru*. The fearsome turtle inhabits the beaches where the *Orinoco* and the *Apure* are twined together; the jaguar, the crocodile come here for meat and poultry which the tortoise provides. The natives gather on these banks during the turtle-rains, when the egg harvest is abundant, but the crocodiles and the tigers wait for the tortoise to lift its head above the surface of the waters. The turtle lays its eggs after sunset, and hides them in holes on neighboring islands, but the jaguar, the saurian, and the vulture pursue them.

The voice of the crocodile is heard during the turtle-rains, when she is calling to her young; when the savannahs are deluged the colt swimming toward the mare is the booty of this beast. The crocodiles of *Angosture* eat men, but in the *Rio Neveri* they do not trouble them; this reptile abhors the *Rio Negro*. Gnats, mosquitos, and the azury *zancudos* scorify human flesh at the *Rio Magdalena*. On the rocks along the banks of the *Cassiquiare* there are figures of the sun, the moon, tigers, and saurians, but these were never translated into Diana, or the Satyrs.

There are bastard seas which have a low and high tide, like the *Champoton* and the *Rio de Lagartos* in Yucatan. These are salty summer waters which make men lethargic, so that their sole concern is an adipose iguana, the sun, or weaving.

*   *   *   *   *

The immense *llanos* are still recent ocean bottom; the *Amazon* is known as a great fresh water sea, but Poseidon must search for Demeter for hundreds of years, because the burning plains are sterile, and the vast masses of polypi, the relics of a fleeing Atlantic, do not season vices, or perfect the soul.

The *Zama*, *Mataveni*, the *Atabapo*, the *Tutuamini*, the *Temi* are the waters of Ham, for they are black; the waters of Joppa are red, but this is Adam's flood; the *Cassiquiare*,

116

which flows into the *Rio Negro*, is white; the two tributaries of the *Cassiquiare* are the *Siapa* and the *Pacimony*, but one is fair, the other dark; the *piritu* palm trees that fringe the black river of the *Atabapo* are thorny palms; Linnaeus asserted that the country of palms was the original abode of man, and that man is by nature palmivorous; the Indians in this region live for months on the fruit of the *piritu* palm trees.

The Portugals canonized the rivers of Brazil, naming them after Raphael and Our Lady, but first waters are reptiles, then they are idols, and later harlots after whom the *Rio Magdalena* was called. The names of the Indian waters, the River of the Stones, of the Toads, and of the Crocodiles, are more learned hydrography.

The New Hemisphere is a great ruin, and its rivers are the holy sepulchres which are as noble as the graveyards of Eridu and Borsippa. The plains of Uruguay are the cemetery of the Megatherium, and the rivers of the western hemisphere are the archives of lost peoples. Savages often have more piercing burial-rituals than civilized nations. Certain Indians have a tradition that wherever they die, they are soon afterwards interred in the hollowed bark of a tree in the bank of a stream. The past of America is as unknown as that site in Mount Nebo where Moses is buried.

Nations are children everywhere, and the rituals in all countries are very much the same, for they are tributary rivers of one great parent stream, Ocean, the father of Earth.

History is honey in the head of Plato; it is told that no dew or rain fell upon the hills of Gilboa after Saul and Jonathan were slain there by the Philistines. Let us take up the pipes, harps, and Psaltries which Jubal gave us and sing our annals; this is Indian pagan land, let us claim it; it is our crib and our deity; our arms are miserable earth, and our hands a thousand sins, and we will be waifs and Ishmaels, utterly kinless, and we cannot come into our own Golgotha, or native agony, until we cry, Abba, Abba, for every river is the descendant of Abraham, Isaac and Jacob.

XIV

THE MISSISSIPPI is the parent of the canes that fringe the banks; the walnut, the mulberry, the maple and oak are homage to the river. This Spirit waters the earth for thousands of leagues of man, and the Indians called this god Mechasipi. Some rabbin of yore or Syriac thinker claimed that the Spirit is three cubits long, but this is Kabbalistic speculation, as the head does not contain so much water, soul, or meditation. Hennepin called it the *Colbert*, and the priest Marquette, *Concepcion*. The stream *Akansa* comforts the aspens, mothers the beans and the medlars; the *Chickasaw* is the house-parent of the laurel, the elm and the mulberry tree. The five lakes are the elders of the continent, but the Fatal River is the Holy Ghost of America.

Rivers are uncured, nomadic waters until they are myths. The *Chicahominy*, the River *Powhatan*, discovered by Captain John Smith, are Indian graves rather than the living vines of waters. When Egypt was first peopled it was a morass, and at the time John Smith arrived in the country of Virginia, there was no grass there except what grew in the marshes. The land and rivers of Louisiana were as bitter as Orcus.

La Salle called the Province he explored Louisiana, which was as vast as the territory of Shem which extended from Jerusalem to India. This region went as far South as the English Carolinas, and its western boundaries were the *Mechasipi*, the Missouris, and the *Obache* River.

Strabo, De Soto and La Salle were river geographers. Man cannot achieve knowledge except what water yields to mortal mind. Truths are in the bitter marshes of the deceased. La Salle had a February genius; he was a cold cosmographer, having fewer vices to moult than Cortes and De Soto. The Cavalier had little of earth, air, fire; he was as dour as the peninsula rock of Araya; mica slate feigns a sterile mien, and is water bottom, but the garnet trembles there. It is doubtful that he ever found the source of the *Mechasipi* which is warm and falls into the Gulf, because character, free will and destiny are the same. La Salle chose Canada, and North America, a Golgotha's Vineyard, as his water and burial site.

Seeking the Fatal River, the French saw tracks of wild goats in some sloughs. The lakes were covered with teal, waterhens, bustards. There were herds of plovers pecking ruined pools. They imagined they were near the Magdalen River. There were rattlesnakes among the brambles which the starved men ate when they could kill them. Alligators slept

120

in the marshes; the musk of this reptile comes from its cod; the meat is white, and sweet, but few of the French had any stomach for it.

* * * * *

At Lake Huron the men dug up acorns under the snow, having no other food. They had planted melons, endive, parsnips, pompions, but the birds and animals ate the seeds. Herbs, vegetables and death came into the world on the third day. Besides the wild garlic in the marshes, and the small onions growing on the mesa, they had no other aliment or solace but the plant of death.

The wolves had left four feet of a deer which the French seethed in the *Pottowattamie* village. Decayed pumpkins, the thongs and the shield of a bison were their rations until they reached *Missilmakinak*.

Brambles and willow were his portion out of which he fashioned withes to knot an otter or beaver. The severest deity is need, a god who confers benefits upon men who toil with chance.

There was no home-coming to Ithaca for La Salle. The waters of Styx flowed through his head. No Calypso detained him in a recondite Orphic cave; the violets, the purslane that sprang up in the bog had never been pacified by Ceres, and the prairie hemp was savage. Polybius says that Menelaus went to Joppa, founded by Japhet, but La Salle, a far greater navigator, discovered cannibal towns, some Indian remnants, the Miamis at the source of the *Teatiki*, the *Outagamia* on the banks of the Green Bay. He had not built one colony, or left any chronicles; murdered by his own men, the journals of his feats were kept by faithful but sterile companions. Father Hennepin endeavored to steal his exploits, and to claim for himself the role of Ulysses or

Jason, but no one can filch the character of another man, or harm his fame. Whoever Homer was there is no other.

Memory is our day of water tutored by want. La Salle sought virgin Tartars, descendants of Prometheus. He returned to Frontenac, but he had not found the Alpha of the River.

Water is death, but man must seek it. All our seeming wakings are the debris of evening waters; most dreams come from mean shallows, and are the digestive rot of secure bottoms; prophecies rise up from the marine depths ancient as the Flood. We are cartographers, unheeding the singing maggots, or bereft of the Angel.

XV

PRIMEVAL POTHERBS send their roots down far; the manna ash run deep into the earth. The Indian is a forest people; the deity of the *Tupi* tribes is called Caypor, a sylvan god who dwells in the woodlands where he hunts pacas and deer. The baboon of the Old World lives on the ground, but the apes of America are arboreal. The Stone Indian sits in the branches and chants to Keetche Manitou before the bison hunt.

This is wild land, undomestic; the natives have a legend of a shaggy tree-Esau, called Curupira, unmentioned in *Genesis*. The Para estuary is a wild water hymn. How long does it take savage ground to produce the damsels of Jerusalem, or

Dido? Praise be Linnaeus for calling a butterfly Hetaera Esmeralda; man is the thrall of an amorous name.

Sow soft fruits in crabbed weather for etesian winds roughen the furrow of the olive. Broom flowers in dry places. Fir, hemlock and the yew are mountain wood, dour is their fruit; these are no treason's summer friends. Gall-oak, sea-bark, hilly ash and poplar were the names of deities and hewn tree-men. Forest is the hope of the disciples; more learned than the fig is wildest ground.

The *Cedrela odorata* of Brazil is the cedar of Lebanon; of jasper, onyx, and garnet are the hues of the Papilio, which Linnaeus has called the Trojan. There is the Morpho Menelaus whose wings are the garments of Asia. The cigana who pecks the arborescent Arum near lagoons is no bird of *Proverbs*. We know the parables of the wheat and the tares, but the genipapa, the goyava, the mandioca remain unsung.

The holm oak, pond apple, and sumac are Indian. Pale Face is a waif among the Sierras and the mesa, a trespasser upon the savannahs. Bog-moss swaddled the Indian infant; the Mechasipi is savage Virgin Mary; the Great Lakes are the five tribes of the Iroquois. The red men of America were not amorists; they had no vehement passion for women. Man is sun, water, earth, air, or depraved; head, arms, feet are ground, sea water, woods, or emptied of them, loveless. Unrelated to the desert, the rivers, the forests, man is feeble and a random fornicator.

* * * * *

Amidst a plethora of oak, maple, streams, hummocks, Pale Face is famished for a tree, a little hill, a foal, a clump of sod; utterly sterile, he begs for the Nature he has warped and killed. He cannot be a thinker, a moral animal, until he returns, as a lover, bringing the peace calumet and the grains of tobacco, as a votive offering, to the cliffs and the wilderness which he threw away.

Every country contains the minerals of Paradise or is the barren ground for rough annals. Art without austere weather emasculates the American. The roots of bed-straw washed in a kettle, with the juice of the moose-berry, and pistils of the larch, provide dyes for the Stone Indians. The bark of the aspen and birch is the food of the beaver; these are Laconian arts and meals.

The bison, red deer and antelope crop the meadows near the sources of the Missouri and Assineboine Rivers, which are the pastures for congealed American philosophy. Snow and ice are the grazing grounds of North American metaphysics. Want is the god of the North, desolation is his child; the otter, beaver, and the musquash were the Buddhas of Thoreau. The hardships of explorers were vast moral experiences; Franklin and Parry opened northern straits, Canaan was fathoming the limestone strata of the Sasketchawan fringed with purple dogwood and dwarf birch, and populated by the pelican and the brown fishing eagle. The marmot carried the seeds of the American vetch in its pouch; the head of the geographer contains the Nelson River, Swampy Lake and New Waters.

Lichen and moss sang in your heart; the forest was your brother, poverty the chaste girdle of your bride. Be hardy, and ashamed; modest birds cover themselves with chaff after pleasure; the goose bathes, and others shake their feathers.

Ariel lies to the south; when the pampas is a cocoa orchard and the vintage of Israel—Brazil, Peru, Uruguay, Chile, will be the timbrels, the sackbut, and the harper of the Americas. Quito, Lima, and Cuzco are handlooms; the Mexican valley shall be the home of Apis; emerald and turquoise are the stones of Rahab.

Why does the gillyflower, resembling the spindle which has the scent of Abel's blood, allure us? Give me marl, or rotten leaves which delight the oxen; so that I can be frugal; or hellebore, or danewort, fenugreek to quell all riot, and drive Apis into exile. The slightest wind blows us over, and everything impregnates men. Anaxagoras says that the air contains all seeds, and each time men take a breath they are fornicators; for rain, sleet and flesh are the planters.

Man is water and parched land; fire and rock are his hopes; desire is the Trade Wind; the fruit of the Tucuma palm is the Arcadia of the macaws, and the ruse of mortals. Pumice stone in the Amazons carry the seed of plants, and spawn of fresh-water fish as they come down from the remote volcanoes, *Cotopaxi* and *Llanganete* of the Andes; four hundred miles from the Atlantic the throb of Poseidon is felt in the *Tapajos* river. For many weeks' journey one cannot find a pebble in the regions watered by the *Solimoens*. The lower Amazon is hilly; on the shores of the *Teefe* are groves of wild guave and myrtles.

Where are the little hills which shall bring justice, or the fruits of Lebanon? O forest spectre, ferns, lichens, boleti contain Eden. Be primordial or decay.

PART II

The Carnal Myth

A Search into Classical Sensuality

I

THE MAJORITY of persons choose their wives with as little prudence as they eat. They see a trull with nothing else to recommend her but a pair of thighs and choice hunkers, and so smart to void their seed that they marry her at once. They imagine they can live in marvelous contentment with handsome feet and ambrosial buttocks. Most men are accredited fools shortly after they leave the womb, and these ninnies are always drunk for women. Sometimes they fall into convulsions over a piece of vermilion cloth wrapped about the bodice of a drab, not perceiving they could have just as well taken for a spouse a swath of red material, and for much less expense and trouble. The salacious zany is enticed by a petticoat or the saffron hair of the pard. These simpletons never cease to hurry after affliction, pain, and lawsuits, and if they have received a patrimony, they at once dissipate it on a chit with the mind of a goose and the avarice of Cleopatra. The harlot has a mouth of honey, warns Solomon, but the wine she gives is heavily paid for later. It is wise to remember that Livia, the procuress for Augustus, was the grandmother of Agrippina, the lupine mother of Nero.

The rabid fornicators are in a great hurry when gendering, and there are many divorces for this reason. At first they are uxorious husbands, and their wives, accustomed to such wanton and unruly attentions, later find the indifference of them insupportable. With this in mind, Aristotle advises men not to give their wives unusual pleasures. The madness for rapturous sensations has brought about countless infidelities, greed, and a plethora of thieves and effeminates. The Egyptians removed the nose of an adulteress; and this showed much wisdom, for no matter how toothsome the mouth is or how soft the haunches, Venus without a nose cannot sustain the most vehement ardor.

Every confusion comes from Eros; clothes and dyes inflame human beings, and Plato was so mindful of this that he said that boys and girls should go into the gymnasium naked as they did in Sparta. The uterus enrages the human race; the mind and the testes are similar to the twins of the Roman spouse Pliny mentions, one resembling her master, and the other the butler.

The rout blame their wives for their own faults. Euripides says: "It is to be expected that the husband of a bad wife be bad." No one can attribute his weakness or vice to another; the flaw is always in one's self, and he who is malicious or vindictive gelds his own mind and person. One can diminish himself but not the knave or the thief by an act of contumely or a fierce retaliation. It is impossible to harm another soul, good or wicked; this is the one part of man that connot be penetrated or grasped.

Poets whose works send men to brothels are themselves becrazed or in constant need of prostitutes. Men have enough to do to toil against vices without being inflamed by books. No one, except a witling, desires to be a profligate; and it is absolute insanity to drop one's seminal strength into new vessels every night. One pines because he did not take a maid who offered herself to him, and he gnashes his teeth because another has received the transitòry spasms of pleasure he has refused. "If I save you, O virgin, will you thank me?" is the compunction of one character in Euripides. In later years men recall their own kind acts with boundless gratitude, but it is as impossible to remember any physical ecstasy as it is to know how Helen of Troy looked. We can only imagine, and even the great poet Homer does no more than intimate that she is beautiful.

Helen had genius, but only knew how to employ it when she had lagging, curried dugs, and long after Ilium had been cindered. As an aging matron, when her thighs and matrix were no longer sharply coveted by mortals, she was a soothsayer and knew how to alleviate the anger or sorrow of a man. A woman who can temper human anguish is a sibyl; Pythagoras thought that metaphysics wore out the heart. Our loins shake when we regard the riggish Helen who has lain in the bed of Paris, but we respect the elder wife of Menelaus more. However, it is fatuous to assume

131

that she could no longer arouse men: Plato had a wrinkled mistress from Colophon; and whether experienced women are systolic or not, they are as lubricous as Clytemnestra. It is idle to think that men who go to older women for pleasure are dotards, and also inane to assume that wisdom is in the young and that Nestor has a doddering mind.

The cult of the body makes women *gery shrewe*, and from such females men beget fops, and dunciads. In a moment of contrition Helen calls herself a bitch. The serving maids of Penelope are, in Shakespeare's word, *brachs*.

Every one develops his vices, few water or nourish one virtue; it is for this reason hard to avoid false or true surmise; no man, when he sees the snare being prepared for him, is willing to believe that the flesh artists, the harlots of sensations, Agrippina and Poppaea, are not affectionate. Poppaea has every skill for the longest and most delirious sexual bout, and her voluptuous understanding is taken for love. She is as cold as the *phagrus*, which has a stone in its head; and when this freezes, the fish falls into a frenzy.

We suspect the odor and decay of fungus and the snail in women but seldom are clever enough to depart from any evil. Women are all our folly; few can walk away from Agrippina, Messalina, or Clytemnestra. Any of these three women has far more aptitude in venery than men. They are the spiders of the human race, and they can draw almost anybody into their webs.

Do you understand the ways of birds, brutes, and bawds? The sparrow stands erect in coition, the hen crouches, the elephant lies on her back, bears hug one another, and hedgehogs face each other. What Agrippina and Clytemnestra had not learned from the sparrow, the hen, the elephant, the bear, and the hedgehog, they acquired from the monkey, who falls into any posture to satiate his lust.

Jupiter gave the Romans seven halcyon days before the winter solstice and seven after it, which is all that flesh can tolerate. Homer says that Ulysses was a waster of cities; scarce married, he left Penelope to pillage Ilium and the beds of Calypso and Circe. Calypso is the sorceress with many girdles, and Circe the sexual snake; the offspring of Circe and Ulysses was said to be immune from the venom of the serpent. Man without the poison of the adder has no intellect, and women lacking it are unable to fold their serpentine loins about Adam. Adam paid no attention to Eve, or even noticed that she was naked, until the snake in the garden gave her the cunning to entice Adam to eat of the Tree of Knowledge, which, alas, bears the fruit of lust.

There are many legends regarding the infidelity of Penelope. She is supposed to be the mother of goatish Pan by one of the wicked suitors. It is also related that Hermes came in the shape of a goat and lay with Penelope, who gave birth to Pan. There are the tales of the poets of the Comedy, who are connoisseurs of the celestial rumps of nymphs and of beef. The later fables about Penelope show a great decline in the chastity of women. Priapus dominates Hellas, and in Caesar's Rome who, save the elders, and Catullus, remember the epithalamium that was once sung when the bride, fragrant with woodbine and marjoram and virtue, was placed in the thalmus.

Troy is sacked for Helen and ore; because Menelaus was a wittol, was it necessary to make a holocaust of mothers, sons, and daughters? For the possession of one particular womb he had to kill the honeycombed town of Asia Minor. Had he a little sense, he would have taken another wife.

Men are either enthusiastic whoremongers or warriors. Faint-hearted Menelaus was good for nothing and was as mediocre in battle as he was in Helen's arms.

The adulterer maims friends and makes of whole races a carcase to recapture the nose, the teats, the secret parts he cannot even memorize. Men fear to give their affections because they have the utmost dread of growing the horns of the wittol. The prey of the conycatcher raises some compassion; the cuckold arouses the laughter of the bulls and the noise of the timbrel. A boar without tusks will not go near the sow, and the cuckold is just as helpless; mistrust breaks his whole nature. He skulks beneath the stones and cohabits mutely without attachment.

Homer tells that Menelaus sprang from the lineage of the Asiatic voluptuary Tantalus, who was too forceless to endow Menelaus with strength. When Agamemnon went to Priam he left a bard to counsel his wife in virtue and abstinence. Agamemnon, also, had been of no more use to Clytemnestra than Menelaus was to the licentious lady of Troy. Aegisthus, the lover of Agamemnon's wife, took the poor bard out to a desert island and killed him so that he could lie with Clytemnestra without hindrance, song, or advice.

There is less trouble in the world when we are reared by streams, animals, trees, as legend says of some of the heroes of Hellenic philosophy. The river Achelous was a parent, and the epical foe of Achilles was the watery Scamander and the river Melos was said to be the father of Homer. Faustulus, the shepherd discovered the infants Remus and Romulus sucking the dugs of a wolf beneath a fig tree. He took them to his wife Laurentia to rear, but it is alleged that she was the strumpet of goatherds and was called Lupa. This fable prepares us for the woeful annals of Rome, but it is not often that the lineage of a people is available or that it is possible to learn whether a nation has sprung from a volcano, a quiet grove of poplars, or from the ribs of Numa. The most valorous men have strong animal origins, and they are the teachers of blushes and modesty.

Man became lascivious when he moulted his feathers and cast away most of his hair. He is now the most beautiful of the animals and, unfortunately, the most alluring. The ass rages for the body though its beauty is as short-lived as the fig and the pomegranate. This leads people to think that exquisite sensibility is the same as feeling; all persons love their own experiences, and those who have unusual art in scenting human skin, asphodels, or the willow are regarded as good and thoughtful.

Naked Diana awakens trembling felicity because she is almost entirely skin. So ridiculous is human desire, she is also highly esteemed because she has heavy hair on her head and but a small nest of it around her secret parts. Others will reject a woman with the hirsute legs of Esau, unless she has an opulent dowry.

Priapus is a scurrile noddy and an ignoramus, and no one can regulate his habits or predict his taste. He is as easily shared by a harpy as by a mermaid. He often prefers a jade with balding eyebrows or a goatish smell. He gathers up odors like corruption. The mother of the Scythian race was a monster, half virgin and half viper; from the buttocks upward she resembled a woman, but she had the lower parts of a serpent.

The more feeble man becomes, the more subtle are his

sexual arts. As he grows in mind, the more fierce is his desire to retain the habits of the beast. Pliny held that, the longer the world lasts, the lesser bodies shall nature produce. The weak demand exceptional orgies. The debilitated man is hard to please, and he has no palate or appetite for a Venus without rare blemishes. Human powers have been declining for many millenniums. Hector guttled away his energies when Ilium was besieged. He went from Andromache's bed straight to battle, and it may be said that it was not Helen but Andromache that destroyed Troy. Hector was an Asiatic epicure, and Andromache was abnormally big which was a reason for the long erotic revels each day before he had to face an Achilles or one of the two bulky Ajaces.

The apple and the unguents are no longer enough; a slattern excites the dandy most, or a seam of hair on the upper lip of Aphrodite, or a rank armpit. Ovid explains that Roman cosmetics came from the part of the wool where sheep sweated most. Woman now, unless she is positively mediocre and has no excessive foible or malady, will not be without a husband.

Libidinous women make the worst wives, for they are testy, and as soon as they have exhausted their husbands, they look for another one. The blood cannot boil all day long; and as wise Pythagoras's niece once said, a woman ought to cast aside her continence when she sheds her petticoats, and resume it again when she puts them on.

Everything comes in twos, good and evil, pleasure and asceticism, life and dying. Hermes is the god of eloquence, and this winged courier brings the right words to the mouth of the poet, and he also tells him when he is to die.

There is no writing, or life, or teaching that is good that is not heavily impregnated with death. Woman is two by nature; chaste Artemis is a midwife, and she assuages the hardships of parturition, but she herself has no children. Daphne preferred to be a tree rather than submit to the embraces of Apollo. Such women, provided they are not cold or glum, are sorceresses, weavers, or steadfast friends.

Hecuba remarks that no one will prefer the bed of Cassandra to the spear of Achilles, and whether she is speaking of courage or not, it has another meaning besides what Euripides gave to it. Agamemnon was puerile in taking Cassandra, for a young prophetess is an ineffectual bed-partner, and she is more likely to be thinking of a treatise on the soul or to ask whether Plato regards the earth as a cube than to be raising her haunches and employing her loins to the best advantage of her beloved.

A virtuous beauty is a plant whose first fruits are bitter, but the roots of her character are fragrant. She is similar to a plant whose power is in all parts of her rather than one. A noble woman has some wintry stone in her. It is not Plutus, greed, that gives, nor a hot drab that retains her husband, but Vesta, who guards the marriage threshold and drives the adulterer away.

Plain feeding makes for lasting, humble wedlock, and according to Dionysius of Halicarnassus, there was not a divorce in Rome for five hundred and twenty years. The first Roman to divorce his wife was Spurius Carvilius, and he was hated forever afterward for this act.

Abigail who has the understanding, carnal heart, relieves David the Psalmist rather than Adonis, and lamed Vulcan, husband of Aphrodite, is more virile and eager for her favors than a coxcomb from Crete.

137

It is preposterous to think that Clytemnestra killed Agamemnon in his bath to get what the weasel and the martin possess. This is the organ that mocks the mind, which dupes the man. For the heart imagines evil that the foot, the hands, and the head cannot know except by dream or accident. Those who despair of the race know that man cannot be seraphic until nature has altered his body. Maybe higher man will be a eunuch. It is a forlorn thought; and while we ponder such a future, in which we can have no share, we thank Zeus for this, who, when he lay with Alcmena, made the night three times as long. Let us weep for Tammuz; bring the first fruits and the white poplar flowers to Priapus; here is wine and oil and balsam for Phallus.

The Nile overflows when the etesian winds blow, and there are heavy rains in Ethiopia at the rising of the Dog Star; but man's desires are out of season and at odds with the little, growing seeds, the bulbs, the tubers and the upswelling sod. There is a time for the crop of kisses, a month for borning and begetting, the season for dirges and sorrow. The wisest planter waits for all things to happen and to come to him. The patient man loves longest and best.

Myrrh, galbanum, and nard are the Shulamite and the griefs thereof. The olive, fig, and the pomegranate are Abigail, and Bathsheba of the Psalmist. Fire, air, water, earth are grass, fungus, and pride. The fruits of Jerusalem and Hellas suffer most from the worm and the caterpillar. Man is a delicate vine bruised by rain, dew, and the zephyr, which give the scab of Venus.

Jacob gave thought to his sons and considered the wolf, the adder, and the ass's colt, and then blessed the breasts

and the vulva. That the suckling of a deer takes aliment from Indian paps is no matter. God bless Sarah, Hagar,
Rebekah, Rachel, and Bilhah, Jacob's concubine whom
Reuben trod; for sufficient unto the day are the nipples and
the womb thereof.

II

MARS AND VENUS are the two pests of humanity.

Men are mad most of their lives; few live sane, fewer die so. Life is a vast solitude, and whether alone or with a wife, man is beside himself, which is to say that he is possessed. The acts of people are baffling unless we realize that their wits are disordered. Man is driven to justice by his lunacy. Otherwise, he boasts of his faults unless necessity has come to him. Primitive people are less insane than the civilized: the Scythians drank the blood of their foes after they had slain them; the cultivated man, less coherent, seldom perceives who is his adversary or his friend, and so he drinks the gore of both. The Greeks who had been pursued by

140

the Persian Tissaphernes for hundreds of leagues across the plains of Asia imagined that, after they had sacrificed a bull, a wolf, a bear, and a ram on a shield, the Persian would not betray them.

Darius the Persian was mad when he attacked the Scythians who had no cities, mines, or arable farms. The Scythians worshipped Vesta as their first deity, which shows a pious regard for chastity. However, a fool on his nuptial night does not know whether he has culled a maidenhead or gotten the pox. The women guarding the temple dedicated to earth were required to take a draught of bull's blood to prove that they had been continent. Democritus of Abdera, seeing a young girl passing by his garden, greeted her with "Good morning, maiden." When he perceived her rushing home at dusk, he cried out, "Good evening, woman."

There is an account of two hyperborean virgins who came to Scythia with sacred knowledge wrapped in wheat straw. The Scythians carried all their laws in their heads, having no need of books. The plays of Terence are about gluttons and parasites, but the Scythians, being too poor to have either, did not require Roman comedies.

The Scythians did not care for water; the western tub is viewed as a dirty douche by the Indians. Hot baths are in many cases surreptitious profligacy. The Scythian women pounded pieces of cypress, cedar, and the incense tree upon a rough stone, which gave off an agreeable odor. Occidental man washes his face, but it looks sour and pasty.

These people had more pious burial rites than do Atlantic citizens, who inter their dead with furtive haste. They opened the belly of the dead, filled it with bruised anise seed, incense, and parsley, and sewed it up so that their last recollection of a mother or father was rustic and aromatic.

A Libyan nomad had no other property than a bowl, a sword, a ewer, and a hut made out of the stalks of the asphodels. The earliest Romans drank from the horns of oxen. Aristotle writes that the Rhodians had drinking cups composed of myrrh, rushes, saffron, balsam, and spikenard, boiled together with clay. This is elysium for those who have no part in it.

The worst calamity to a people is luxury, for Plutus is luxury which is brutal greed which leads to the deflowering of the strength, the virtues, and the dryads of a country. The Scythians lived in frugal wooden towns, abhorring the Grecian bacchanal, for they considered dissipation a woe. Barbaric nations have no spital houses, conycatchers: when a Libyan child had a fit the mother gave him the urine of a he-goat. The old primitive Christ, with an ass's head, and Jupiter, who was in part a ram, are for the poor. The meek shall inherit the earth because the avaricious, having polluted it, go in demented herds, looking everywhere for more ground, like Demeter wandering after her daughter, Persephone.

O man, take nothing from the earth, our mother, without a prayer, and be not hurried, for waiting is history, which is always seated like contemplation and Buddha.

War is an iambic rage; battle is the amour of the insane, the voluptuous entertainment of the tyrant. Despotism comes from the insatiable belly and the scrotum. Since men are at war most of their lives, Homer could hardly write about them in any other manner. Homer knew what men liked to do best, and the *Iliad* is the record of it. Conflict is the fable of man, and those who make the chronicles of the acts of Agamemnon, Achilles, Xerxes, or Alexander of Macedon are mythographers.

After Darius had conquered the Scythians, who were standing at attention in his presence, a hare ran by, and the nomads, thinking nothing of the victorious Darius, ran after the hare to catch and cook him. The Persian king was sorely vexed, because he had sacked paupers who thought more of a hare than of Darius. The asses in Darius's camp showed more generalship than he; they were so wanton that they entirely confused the horses of the Scythians when the latter, in a retaliatory skirmish, came to assault Darius's troops.

When Darius sent messengers to Greece, demanding earth and water, the Athenians cast one into a pit and the other into a well, saying, "Here are earth and water for Darius!"

At the time Darius fled from the battlefield, he escaped the pursuing hosts of Alexander because he rode a mare who was eager to return to her colt, for she had recently foaled.

The Persian rulers were exemplary madmen, rarely falling into moments of good judgment. Darius, Cambyses, and even Cyrus were deranged most of their lives; Xerxes was insane all day long. Xerxes and his wife, Amestris, were poets of carnage; they are the wild parsley or water hemlock of the human race. Xerxes came to Greece with countless female bakers, concubines, eunuchs, and Indian dogs, and his army resembled an effeminate, Asiatic belly at table. This host of men dried up streams, and entire cities prepared flour and meal for many months, fattened cattle and fowl in coops and ponds, to feed his troops.

The Athenians, hearing reports of this titan stomach that was marching toward them, went to the oracle at Delphi and were informed that they would be destroyed by Xerxes.

When grief, disaster, or the jealousy of others overtake men, they are as helpless as the Romans, who, after the Tiber had washed away their houses and myriads of citizens, could do little else than consult the Sibylline Books.

Two oracles are better than one. When the Athenians saw that they were doing nothing but shaking with dread of Xerxes—and this is no condition in which to make ready for any fate—their messengers returned to the Delphian god, who delivered a more ambiguous report concerning the future of the Greek cities.

When man is in doubt regarding his soul or the strength of his character, he will labor for his destiny, which is what the Greeks did; and their triumph over Xerxes cost them less than a few hundred men.

Xerxes' army was senseless passion, but Xerxes was a dithyrambic lunatic. Enraged with the Hellespont for destroying the bridges of white flax and papyri constructed by the Phoenicians and Egyptians who were with him, he ordered that the strait be given three hundred strokes. When Xerxes was on board ship and a storm arose, he asked his pilot what could be done to prevent the vessel from sinking. After he was told that there were too many men on board, he asked the superfluous Persians to show their loyalty to their king by jumping overboard and drowning themselves. Later Xerxes gave the pilot a handsome present for saving his life but had him beheaded for diminishing the number of Persians in his army.

The Persians soon ate up Greece and were quickly afflicted with hunger and dysentery; they had no food but bark, leaves, and the boiled ropes of their beds. At war the needy Persians had behaved like demigods and the most frugal Pythagoreans, Ebionites, or Essenes. They healed their wounds with myrrh, and their table was even more bleak than that of the sages.

Xerxes was as ecstatic at home as abroad; he feared his wife Amestris more than he did the Greeks, and so committed two follies. Being a poor soldier, he was inordinately licentious, living like Silenus in the garden of Midas, where the roses were unbearably fragrant. He conceived a tormenting passion for his brother's wife. He could not seduce her, and he was unwilling to ravish her, for what exquisite reasons one cannot determine. Imagining he could draw her more closely to him through even a more intimate family connection, he arranged to have her daughter marry his son. Such a marriage would result in children, and this would bring the much-coveted mother to the palace and to his private apartment.

Venus is adroit in humbling the man who desires her, and Mercury himself is poor of tongue when Venus slips her heel out of her sandal. A philosopher may know the weather of the stars, but it will avail him nothing when Aphrodite strokes her skirt. Woman's body is her wisest mind, against which man is raving dust. At her mirror and her cosmetics, she is the poet of affectations: her pomade, stybium pot, and jewels garnish her wiles. She is almost an impeccable dissembler. Of all the brutes in the earth she is the best artist with her flesh.

The son of Xerxes married the daughter. The felicity of Xerxes was unimaginable, and his rapture was unendurable, for he immediately fell in love with the daughter, who accepted him!

In his delirium Xerxes asked his new daughter-in-law what

she wanted most. He was prepared to present her with four thousand square miles of sterile Scythian territory, the River Nile, and a thousand vineyards. She asked for nothing except the mantle Amestris had woven for him. The Persian king was dumfounded and offered her the command of an army, the revenue of ten handsome cities, and much gold. She had no intention of pouring down her lissome throat the Persian Gulf or the Nile. She had the most genuine love for him and desired only what he feared most to give her.

Xerxes gave her the mantle. When it came to the ears of Amestris that her daughter-in-law was wearing the cloak she had made for her husband, she conceived a mortal hatred for the mother of the daughter. This was a very reasonable passion: Was not the goat who conceived the kid at fault rather than the adulteress, since she could not have been troublesome had she not been born? Amestris had long since passed her jocund season, and the flesh that once had entertained Xerxes was now wrinkled. Amestris had taken fourteen children of the best Persian families and buried them alive as a holy sacrifice to the earth. She hated seedtime and all the darling, good fruits of the sun.

Once a year on the king's birthday a great festival was given, and on this occasion a monarch could not deny the petitioner whatever he desired. Amestris came to the banquet and demanded as her present the mother. Xerxes at once summoned his brother, who was married to the mother, and said, "Don't cohabit with your wife any more, but take instead my daughter," but the brother of Xerxes replied, "Sire, I like to lie with my wife," a remark which infuriated Xerxes.

Xerxes, like Zeus, had sex all over his body, and could bring forth Minerva from his head or Bacchus from his thigh. Still, he was as helpless as Zeus, who loved Troy, for gods that have genital organs are as foolish as men, and as unreliable. This the Persians knew, for they paid the highest prices for eunuchs because they said they were faithful.

It is not certain why Xerxes was anxious to save the life of his brother's wife, except that he still pined for her, since he had possessed everything else, and a tyrant can never be satisfied. Meanwhile, Amestris instructed the bodyguards of Xerxes to take the mother, cut off her breasts, ears, nose, and hands, and then return her to her husband. When the brother of Xerxes saw his wife so mutilated and slain, he went to Bactria and there raised a revolt, and for his perfidy Xerxes slew him.

At the time Cyrus came to the throne, he realized that the Persians had grown effeminate and weak through excessive gendering and feeding on whole camels. He said that a country that has delicate fruits produces delicate men rather than valiant soldiers. Understanding their error, they left the soft vineyards and the fertile plains and repaired to a hard, barren country. To be strong and rough for war, they lived like Diogenes, who was content with a barley cake and who said that the best appetizer was hunger!

* * * * *

Man is a martial animal, either riggish or bored, and only half-domesticated. Battle and gain are his religious amusements. Man casts away peace for war, for Ilium, Helen, pelf and copulation.

Epical companionship is the hymn of Ares; it is battle and strife; one must be as prepared for truth, love, or a friend, as Diomedes was ready at all times for rapine, sleeping on a hard bed with upright spears planted near enough to grasp them. Chrysostom said that the Thebans bore the marks of spears on their bodies, which had been left by the dragon's teeth Cadmus had sown. As man is a negative animal, legends and history inform us that he is seldom trustworthy except in battle. "War is the father of progress," says Heraclitus, a stygian augury.

We do not admire the wrath of Achilles, nor Ajax the dolt, nor the violence of Alexander of Macedon. The latter, however, was the perfect predacious brute. War was the orphic occupation of Alexander, one of his Muses; Minerva is the goddess of battle and wisdom. Ezekiel, Amos, Plato, Moses, and Christ teach us what man should do; Alexander informs us what he is. His disposition was a marvel among men; niter cleanses the sinner; murder purged Alexander. When he razed the city of the Getae to the ground, he paid his vows to the River Ister; the corrupt, too, speak of the angels. After slaying Clitus, one of the Hundred Companions, he kept to his tent for three days without food or drink. He had the same passion for his friend Hephaestion that Achilles showed Patroclus. When Hephaestion died, Alexander crucified the physician who attended him; and to garnish his funeral ecstasies, he made a dionysiac pyre of an entire town of innocent inhabitants. After pillaging the Ephesians, he forced them to be dutiful to the gods by giving annual tribute to Artemis.

Alexander extirpated Thebes, sparing the house of the poet Pindar. After his Bacchic siege of the Thebans, he sacrificed three boys, the same number of vestals, and three jetty rams to appease the Theban manes. He mimicked the deeds of Achilles and said his mother Olympias was the descendant of Triptolemus, son of Achilles, and he was reported to have worshipped the grave of Priam because he was the father of Hector. Alexander once ran naked around the tomb of Achilles. He paid his vows to the fifty Nereids, the most renowned of whom were Calypso, Amphitrite, and Thetis, the mother of Achilles.

Alexander was indifferent to women; Babylon, Arabia, Palestine, India, Africa were his meal. When one of the Companions spoke of the beauty of Darius's wife, Alexander said he had no desire to see her. Agamemnon sacrificed his daughter, Iphigenia, to appease Diana, showing the little concern he had for the fruit of the womb. Men may waste away for the favors of women, which at least is a logical greed, but no one can fill his gullet with several seas and continents or has the human strength to walk once around a domain that includes Asia and Europe. This is cold venery, and the most difficult to understand. If a man drinks two or three gallons of wine, beer, or ordinary water, he is a sloven bladder. What can any mortal do with seven oceans? This greed is as droll as the junk cony of Patagonia, at the door of whose burrow lies a breccia of bones, dung, shells, or a clock or skewer he has pilfered from a neighboring house.

Every man who cannot be Aristotle would like to be Alexander of Macedon. He destroyed the oldest cities in the earth, and ravaged annals precious to sane mortals. Tyre, meaning the "rock," *tsor*, in Hebrew, he overthrew, and ransacked Phoenicia which comes from the Greek word *phoinix*, or palm tree. The Macedonian king seized Cyprus, a Tyrian colony of Hittites, who furnished King Solomon with numerous wives. The Tyrians who took refuge in the temple of Hercules he pardoned, because he regarded himself as a descendant of that hero. Thirty thousand of these Canaanites, mostly women and children, were sold into slavery.

The *Iliad* he knew by heart, and held games in honor of the Muses. Alexander prized friendship, calling his best generals the Hundred Companions. In a dream he saw a swallow perched upon his head, and at once suspected that the Hundred Friends were conspiring to kill him. His sooth-sayer, Aristander the Temisian, quieted him by telling him that the swallow is a loquacious bird and signified an informer who would disclose the plot against him. A familiar of every crime, he believed that each person had his own vices.

Man is unstable all the days of his life; most of his acts are contrary to his interests. He is the spoiler of his own good fortune because he cannot wait for it. He relies either upon everybody or on no one. The fool has confidence in all people; the knave trusts himself. He seldom knows when he is cuckolded or who is his conycatcher.

The best commonwealth is one in which every citizen governs himself well. Alexander was a saturnalian Spartan. He had seizures of self-abnegation. When the daughters of Darius were his captives, he did not touch them; going through the desert, he refused water because his soldiers had none; at the same time he rode through the burning sands playing a flute and clothed in the habit of Dionysus. Though he worshipped Bacchus, he destroyed Thebes, which was sacred to that god. On Mount Meros, named for Zeus's thigh, in which Bacchus grew, Alexander and his Macedonians celebrated the drunken Revelry for ten days. Obviously he disciplined himself when he had the appetite for it, particularly after he had destroyed twenty cities or had killed a friend. He could not tolerate any opposition and hanged two thousand Tyrians by the seashore for no other cause except that he was unable to capture that formidable rock in the sea as quickly as he had expected. The kite, owl, and sea pie are antagonists to the raven, but there is no one who hates one man so much as another does.

Gaza fell down before him, and the infant and the mother were driven into bondage. He cut holes into the feet of Batis, the brave defender of Gaza, and put brazen rings through them, after which he dragged Batis behind his chariot in imitation of Achilles, who had done this with the corpse of Hector. At Memphis he bowed down to Apis, who had never shown much interest in him. He had also taken possession of the city of Priapus, but it was a bootless spoil. It may be that he gave grave offense to Bacchus, in whose nocturnal ceremony the women hold the phalloi aloft, because he lacked this kind of energy. Alexander of Macedon had the body of Adonis, but this was a god whom the Pythagoreans and the Greek poets did not consider very potent. Venus was supposed to show Adonis her favors, but she is not a wise goddess.

Alexander kept three hundred and sixty-five concubines, who followed his army, because it was a Persian custom. He had adopted the livery of Darius, wearing the purple vest, loose scarlet trousers, and a robe of regal hue. He plundered Babylon, Susa, Egypt, Ecbatana, the empire of the Indies, to garb himself in the colors of the goose.

Alexander laid waste to a great part of his army to smell the myrrh trees and roots of nard in the country of the Ichthyophagi, or the fish-eating Gadrosians. He had the most poignant desire to overcome this impoverished land, where the inhabitants lived in hovels made of mussel shells and roofed with the backbones of fishes. The principal food of these beggars was fish, which he forbade them to eat since this is not regarded as a heroical diet in the *Iliad*. Homer, according to ancient writers, thought the fish in the Hellespont was poor for eating. But then, Alexander's Greek was clumsy.

The raven in Greenland feeds on the offals of seals, and its meat is disgusting; the skin of Alexander was as fragrant as Syrian spices. Babylonian fields were covered with frankincense; cinnamon was torn from shrubs, and the wild meadows produced spikenard. Grief, battles, and murder were Homeric rituals and aromatic plants for Alexander; at the time of the vintage thrushes, glutted with nutmegs, fall down to the ground drunk. Alexander, as intoxicated as a thrush, swollen with nutmegs, ached to seize indignent Mount Meros, which had furnished Dionysus with ivy; he overcame savage Mount Caucasus, where asafoetida, which delights goats, was abundant and terebinths grew on the barren flanks. Belus, the deity of Babylon, had predicted that he would meet his fate in that land, but Alexander, plucking his words from Euripides, answered, "The best prophet is he who guesses well."

Alexander was as crapulous as our passions. He burnt the palace at Persepolis because Thais the harlot urged him to do it. Parmenio, one of the Companions, asked him why he was destroying his own property. The Uxians, impecunious nomads, fell before his javelins. Who goes to war with poverty or loots Lazarus for his gold? It is an absolute delusion to go out into the world with an immense, rich army to pillage gravel.

Had Alexander of Macedon moral faculties, Seneca would have been his poor counterpart. The moral behavior of the alpine daw is different from that of the carrion crow; the two are almost alike, the former having a smaller bill and a sniveling cry. If we understood the anatomy of character as much as the ornithologist knows the sundry species of birds, it would be possible to distinguish between Peter and Judas. Were the tail of the magpie shorter and were there no white in his plumage, he would be a crow. The conduct of the feathered tribes can be ascribed to the craw, the talons, and how they employ their mandibles. Pascal said that the history of the ancient world was the result of the shape of Cleopatra's nose.

The jay, raven, crow, and magpie are robbers, having the disposition of Sisyphus and Alexander. The jay could be taken for a frugivorous Essene did he not prey upon the young of other birds. The nutcracker closely resembles the jay, but he has a different bill, and he dwells in the mountains and is content with the kernels of pine tops. The abode of birds, whether they are mountain dwellers, or love glades, or are pernicious, depends upon the contour of their chaps, rumps, and the color of their plumage.

Alexander was as vehement as the jay, and as crafty as the magpie. The jay, unable to fill his gullet with all the filberts, chestnuts, and sorbs he craves, buries what he cannot eat. The acorns which he has hidden, but cannot remember where, spring up as oaks. The jay is a wastrel, and at times is so violent that he gets his head entangled between two branches and hangs himself. One observer saw a bird tied to a tree who endeavored to peck a morsel, but each time a magpie swept the food away with his tail. The magpie prattles as much as Socrates, but is malicious.

Socrates and Paul, who had doughty bodies and amorous blood, but powerfully tethered, were testy; knew we more of their physical structure, we might better understand how to distinguish between the owls of Judea and Attica. Our knowledge of the anatomy of Alexander is as meager. He marvelled at all origins and sailed down the Hydaspes to the great sea looking for the source of the Nile. Mammals and birds astonished him. When Bucephalus disappeared, he threatened to extirpate the whole Scythian nation if his horse were not returned. He imposed a severe penalty upon anybody who slew the peacock of India. He killed thousands of Indians, but this did not delight him as much as did the elephants he found pasturing near the river Indus.

Stony, bare places gemmed his intellect. He took possession of a rock inhabited by the barbaric Sogdianians, and seized a sterile site known as the rock of Chorienes. There was a legend that Hercules had been unable to capture the rock called Aornus. Alexander overcame this massy stone. Had he an ominous dream, or did some one fall ill, such as Coenus, his friend, he poured out libations to the river gods who wear fillets of sedge and who were known as Nereus and Amphitrite; this was metaphysics as well as murder.

When Alexander lay in his tent groaning because he had murdered Clitus, Anaxarchus told him he was as just as his father Zeus. Anaxarchus had given offense to two deities: justice, which is philosophy, and the bastard Muses, for he was a poetaster. Many escape the one vengeance of the Muses (otherwise how could so many bad writers flourish?), but none can avoid the wrath of justice. Later, Anaxarchus offended Niocreon, king of Cyprus, who had him pounded to death in a mortar.

When Hephaestion died, Alexander had all the manes of the mules and horses shorn, and cut his own hair, because this was the way in which Achilles mourned over the corpse

154

of Patroclus. The Cosseans he burnt alive, offering them as a funeral pyre to the shades of Hephaestion. Slaughtering thousands of Persians, he tortured the Magians, who had not protected the tomb of Cyrus, son of Cambyses. Self-abnegation was also one of his frenzied rites, when an Indian gymnosophist, failing in health, had resolved to die, he prepared the faggots for him, and as the Indian philosopher Calanus lay down in this funeral bed of fire, the Macedonian soldiers uttered the war cry, trumpets were sounded, and the elephants snorted.

After a drunken revel, Alexander plunged into the Tigris, and grew a fever; he endeavored to cure the fatal drowsiness by baths, swimming, offering sacrifices to the gods, and more drinking bouts. Seven of the Companions, seeing Alexander's life ebb away, slept in the temple of Serapis, entreating that deity for help. Ares was his god, and not Apis, Busiris, or Mnevis, for the bull in the Serapeum was not concerned with his destiny.

Who wears the garments that smell of myrrh, aloes, and cassia gives little thought to his last hour. We either drink up our force or meditate upon the banks of Cocytus. Either we live for our end, or we are tempted. It is noble, says Pascal, to be weary and worn out by the vain pursuit of the true and the good. All other fatigue is lust and the tears of the dotard.

When Alexander died, rumor girdled the earth. There was a report that Aristotle, who had been his tutor, had sent a poison, sealed in the hoof of a mule, which had brought an end to the Macedonian conqueror. The bones were scarce cold before the Companions killed each other; Olympias, his mother, was assassinated; Roxana and her issue by

Alexander were murdered; another widow and son, Barsine and Hercules, were destroyed.

Alexander sacked the greater part of the globe for the spices of the Moluccas, pelf, destruction of whole nations, reverently titled history, which is the idolatry of power, gore, and war.

III

SOCRATES advised men not to involve themselves in useless inquiries about how the world was produced. Cosmology is a marvelous sickness of the intellect, and geography is her handmaiden. Strabo showed the greatest veneration for Homer's knowledge of rivers, seas, and lands. The sea is deceitful, as Homer and Virgil teach, and men who spend their time like Thales, the metaphysician of water, or as Anaxagoras musing upon the Cosmos have marine dispositions, and could they be fathomed one would find that the images and ideas at their watery bottom were of the shape of prehistoric fish or of primeval ocean substance.

Pelagic men smell of foam, kelp, bridle weed; their ideas and handshake come from sea olives and sea thyme, which sprout stones in the gulf. The sole labor of the water mind is to find out what is primal. Salt is older than the Deluge, and the meditative man is brackish. Cranes from Scythia fly each year to the salty bogs; the Nile, one of the first rivers in the world, begins in the saline marshes.

Human faculties have their summer solstice and their February dirges; the mind is neither water, shell, skin, nor fire. It is good and then evil, savage and domestic. Austere minds produce wormwood, which thrives in cold regions; the olive on wintry mountains is barren. The ocean intellect has original force; the sea oak grows on stones and oyster shells but has no roots, and is without affections. Seaweed tangles the Pillars of Hercules, where the swag-bellied tunny eats Mediterranean acorns. In the beginning were the great waters and fuci, and after that came mud, the masts, and the fat, sun-loving tunny.

Oceanic seers are mammoths of inhuman wisdom, riverine savants come second; earthy thinkers are social; of fire are the phoenix and sphinx wrought. Heraclitus remarks that a dry soul is the wisest.

Socrates was a rigid Spartan, enduring privations to which no Athenian slave would submit, but his frugal habits were the result of reflection. Socrates was boastful, even a quibbler, as Timon said, and sensual. Balded by lechery, or seeming so, Socrates is dear to our bawdy blood. Plato was a charming poet when he has the knavish but clever Alcibiades portray Socrates as a Silenus in a statuary shop, which when opened up reveals a golden deity.

The life of Socrates is a lesson to the soul because he had every human defect, but unlike the many he was himself the mastiff, Cerberus, guarding the gates of his own hell, where our sins roam without heads of substance. Philosophy is the watchdog of man and is what Plato, Socrates, and Cicero meant when they said that this was the study of death and that Charon is the boatman of the ontological thinker.

When Socrates came to a summer ground strewn with grass and a plane tree, he thought such a place was sacred to Achelous and the Nymphs. Before leaving the tranquil spot, he prayed to Pan, entreating that rustic divinity to unite the inward soul with his exterior nature.

Once Socrates asked one of his sons, Lemprocles, whether it was worse to be hurt by a beast than by the kicks and biting of his mother. Not without boorish appetite, he regarded every exceptional outburst, whether it was anger, pleasure, avarice, or overeating, as forms of violence and disorder. He is said to have shown only one face. Aristippus, the Cynic, thought pleasure the greatest good and pain the greatest evil. Anthisthenes, a pupil of Socrates, asserted that he would rather go mad than feel pleasure. Socrates abhorred whatever unduly aroused him. When Critias the Tyrant was among the company of many of his hearers, Socrates told Critias that all he cared to do was to rub upon Euthydemus as swine scrape themselves against stones.

Socrates gave Aspasia amorous instructions; he told her how to exact the utmost gratulation from coition. This is the hot teaching, perhaps, of Pluto's and Xenophon's droll in the Agora. For he went barefoot in the snow, and endured the most sparse eating.

That he lay with Aspasia or was sorely tempted by Alcibiades is also, we suspect, apocryphal.

Neither Meletus nor Anytus, the accusers of Socrates, ever

said that he traduced boys or was a concupiscent teacher. There is the story related by Diogenes Laertius that, after Socrates took the hemlock, Meletus was given the death sentence and that the Athenians closed the Palaestra and gymnasia, and no one would go to drink at the same public fountains with the former treachers of Socrates. This is probably apocryphal because races of people are not penitent, and when they erect a brazen statue to a man they have killed, they pretend that the honored dead sage was never ridiculed, or banished, or put to death by them. A statue is a wily subterfuge, and a concealment of a truth, and few can look through the bronze to grasp the real occurrence or the man it hides.

The talker is the most trustworthy of men, for though he may often be a bore, he is not likely to be a deceiver. Anthisthenes remarked that his greatest luxury was his leisure, which he employed to be with Socrates. When Zeno arrived in Athens, he went to a bookseller who was reading aloud Xenophon's *Memorabilia*, on Socrates, and, learning that such an extraordinary man had lived in Athens, decided at once to settle there. Socrates never went to the Agora until he thought it was full of people who would hear him. When he was rebuked for saying the same thing over and over again, he answered that, if it were true, he would never tire of repeating it. It is no exceptional grace for a man whose tongue is generally shut to govern it. We would commend a Lacedaemonian for speaking, or laughing, or shaking hands, for by doing so he would be exercising his will. Were Diogenes to hold his tongue, we should praise him for his modesty. A man without appetite cannot be called virtuous because he does not rule desires that never molest him. But the gossipy tongue is an asp, for in one way or another, and often without forethought, it stings.

Babbling is as wanton as the salacious sparrow, who, according to Aristotle, is very short-lived because it cohabits excessively. But it is not the worst of faults, for no man who is garrulous conceals his meanest purposes, whereas it is hard to know whether it is the pard or the fox in the taciturn nature that is lying in wait to spoil men of their wives, property, or composure.

Plato was concerned with justice, ideal conduct, and the government of human passions, and that is what politics or any good commonwealth is about; tyranny is insolence, intractable conceit, greed, and the despisal of saying plain things simply. As Euripides says, not in obscurity but in plainness is wisdom.

There is little or no homage to Aphrodite in the *Laws*, and it is doubtful that Plato was worried about the cessation of his carnal appetites; and if he was at odd moments stung by the sight of an undergarment of one of the flute girls he introduces into the *Symposium*, he either wrote another dialogue or went to the nearby cemetery, which was then the haunt of the Athenian prostitutes, and rid himself of such a plague as quickly as possible. The life of Plato is as much of an enigma as the Beatrice of Dante, who placed the sacred amorists in the Seraphic Circle in his Paradise.

Aristotle had lubricious inclinations, for he investigated the sexual inclinations of sea animals and went to much trouble in finding out whether one fish is given to buggery at the rising of Arcturus or a mullet is best to eat when pregnant. It is not how many profligate aches a man has but with what hardihood he withstands them that draws us to him. Everybody with a warm stomach hears the sirens, and some stuff their ears with books as Odysseus sealed the ears of his sailors with wax.

Plato received all his thoughts from Apollo, the healer, and his son Asclepius and the goddess Artemis, whose name is derived from sound health. She is the most continent of the deities. Aristotle, the great pupil of Plato, was not so temperate as his master. He had all the defects of a poet, often going about in the loud garb of Bacchus and wearing rings. He was so enamored of the concubine of a tyrant that, when the latter permitted him to marry her, he offered a sacrifice. He died at sixty-three, which is a short life for a metaphysician.

We must be on guard against Aeschylus, one of the wisest of seers, because he was a drunkard; when he was a youth, he was once looking at a grapevine until he fell asleep and saw Dionysus, who told him to write tragedies. A philosopher is similar to the oak that bears acorns at the summit and bees in the middle, as Hesiod writes, for the thoughts are the top of a man and are the best fruits of his days, and if he obeys what is highest in him, his nature will flow honey. Xenocrates was said to have had such a severe face that Plato continually told him to pray to the Graces.

A grum man is hard to endure; Demosthenes had a crabbed brow, and he had a disposition that was more suitable locked up in a closet than for sociable purposes. Without strength it is almost impossible to be genial. Aristophanes says that the Athenians did not like hard and sour poets, and let us not set aside the venereal fruits of Helios or the olive that is nourished by Selene, for he who dishonors the sun or the moon and their children the grape, the pomegranate, and the olive is wicked.

The greatest wits, says Aristotle, mentioning Socrates,

Plato, and Hercules, were melancholy, but not dour. Melancholia is a disease which tires the blood. Aristotle thought that happiness is energy, but few are content to be free of these waters and winds which, according to Plato, were later called catarrh and flatulence. The wrath of Achilles we know; and one may hide until his anger is passed, or absent oneself from his person for a month or so, going to the salt depths of the Aegean sea, for brine is a marvelous simple and the dearest of cures to the heart that has been bruised by the ire or indelicacy of a friend.

Sages lose the young blush of Diana or Hippolytus but retain their faculties until death. Hippias had a most acute memory until one hundred and eight, when he died. There is no tale regarding the dotage of Plato, and though the *Laws* are void of those animal images that are known as Pan, the Satyrs, and Silenus, there is severe sagacity in this last song, his senilia, the fabled dirge of the dying swan.

The mind ages or is as deciduous as the tree which sheds its old leaves and is rejuvenated after its sere boughs are broken. The wise sit upon the ground; grapes and the gourd mature when they are clothed in dust.

At sixty one should relinquish pleasure; at fifty, prepare for abstinence or else be ready, as Plato says, to educate his diseases. Aristotle thought that reading was the viaticum of old age, and books are a far more lasting delight than the bed of Helen for whom the Trojans and Greeks became paupers. Xenocrates, one of the scholarchs of the Academy after Plato's death, was abstinent if not ascetic; when Phryne the courtesan crept into his bed with him, she had nothing to say afterward that could add to her rumored abilities.

Dionysius of Heraclea gave a banquet to his sycophants,

and there were many female dancers present, but when the most edible girl approached him, he turned to one of his pickthank friends with the following words: "You take her, I am no longer able." This is a grievous hardship, and the wise so suffer, too, though they cannot derive much satisfaction from such illogical grief. One of the wittiest hetaerae of Athens said that philosophers and poets also knocked on her door.

Ambition kills the rout and utterly ossifies the old, and as Euripides asserts, it is the worst of all the gods. Men with nothing in their heads but the desire for longevity and gain show years which fruit spite and usury. These people never toil for a single truth. God showed Solomon the highest favor because he asked for understanding rather than a long life. Solon reproached Mimnermus, the poet, who said that sixty years was enough for any man, but he was very bored and had already worn out his genitals. Solon wanted to live to eighty, which is about as long as the life of a cocoa tree; and oaks and whales are more long-lived than Xenophanes or Hipparchus, but the former are far more patient and quiet than Mimnermus. Who would not rather be leviathan than Job? There are tribes among the people of India who eat rice loaves, dwell in soft ground nourished by warm winds, and live to be one hundred and fifty years old. This, at least, is what the ancient geographers assert, though some are fabulists.

Few, young or old, struggle to be Solon or Pittacus or Bion. It requires more bravery to overcome the weariness and lassitude of old age than to go into the battlefield. Generally, the aged have a bedlam mind and are no more than wizened or bulky matter, without thought of the universe and of the beginnings of man. When one ceases to wonder, one has

164

perished or, worse, decayed. "Wonder is the beginning of philosophy." said Plato.

The multitude are content to achieve seventy-five or eighty years without acquiring ruth or valorous conceptions. All they have to show for a toothless mouth or wrinkles is money and a debris of household possessions. What is abominable in aging men is not their ague, their cold, shaking blood, but their indifference to learning; they know nothing about Sirius, the winds, mountain laurel, or when vetch should be planted. A medieval author has written: Abishag the Shunammite alone kept the old David warm, since the love of wisdom does not desert its lover even when the body grows feeble. We hear with much desolation the waning amorist of the *Sonnets* and lament the many lustra that lie upon Euripides, who was said to have lived alone in a cave overlooking the sea at Salamis.

It is balm to decaying blood to learn that the courtesan Phoenix came to the bed of decrepit Nestor, but it is inane to sigh for the strength of a runner at the time when one should be a philosopher. Cicero mentions Milo of Crotona, who, while observing prize fighters at their exercises, shed tears over his own dead arms instead of going into similar mourning for his head. The ignorant always want to be boys; Proclus of Naucratis became the partner in the pastimes of his sottish son, who was dissipating the patrimony breeding fighting cocks, quails, puppies, and horses, and imagined that he was a spruce blade when he was only as porcine as his young son. There is more nonage among the youth than in the old in years.

Curried flesh is testy and covets what is lost, the gross, harsh tufts of hair of the hyena or the complexion of the naiads. This is not the time when Lais of Corinth would take a poet's wisdom instead of his obols for pay or Aspasia would lie with Socrates though he had not a pair of shoes on his feet. Men fear to wax mouldy as much as they shake at the thought of the ditch of Tartarus. Few care for the repose of Aeschylus, who had a tough, hairless cranium which only a rock dropped by an eagle could break. Euripides, too, moans: "Youth is ever sweet to me, old age lieth heavier than Etna."

The aged, without minds, are seasoned in falsehoods and petrified by greed, and habit has lain in their acid, trade skins so long they are incapable of rousing their faculties for any intellectual conflict whatsoever. They abhor difficult or abstract ideas, and when they hear of a chivalric conception, they are baneful Hecubas, swearing at a good thought as though she were a fury garlanded with blood and serpents. It is a perversion of the will to detest erudition.

Not many men in their middle life make new attachments; they spend most of their thoughts wailing by the walls of Jerusalem for Tammuz, which is a lamentation for their laggard tail. Shakespeare sorrowed more for his declining phallus and the filberts of groveling Caliban than he did for Ariel. In one of the tragedies of King Richard he has written: "How strange it is that desire outlasts performance."

There is no bile that so sings as in wasted and dissolute flesh; Tiberius, stale with murder, was in his seventies a Libertine, and he had more energy and genius for malice when the worms were impatient for his purulent body than when he was young, because he knew so much more. Old men have rotten, broken dreams, which are omens of their end and the foul labor of their suns and moons. How our dreams persecute us when our appetites are reechy and bloated!

166

IV

MAN DREADS that he may become a dotard, and that his soul may be rifled of the passions of Gethsemane. Scholars relinquish their vigor and harm their intestines to find out that the whelk has the trumpet of a triton or that dolphins couple rubbing their bellies together. There is no parturition without agony; the ova of the fish *Belone* cannot get out of her stomach except by bursting it.

The philosopher increases his knowledge as he rots; there is a sort of wolf spider who impairs her womb to furnish the material for warp threads. How noble it is to decay growing wise; oysters are generated in scummy foam around ships that have been moored a long time.

Most men close to their demise are gross sumpter-asses of business; the valiant die myriads of times, and after the reflective faculties have accomplished their work, they grow trite and fall into dotage. Bees, almost extinct, are restored to life by covering them with ox paunches and mud; the body of a horse can bring a wasp back to life. When the hides of seals are flayed and stripped from their bodies, they comprehend the tides. How sentient are the dead, and of what incalculable value is a corpse to the universe!

Melancholy or distempered elephants tear up grass, which refreshes the soul far more than the pellets of Aesculapius, which makes cowards of whole races. It is good to die casting up grass toward heaven, and he who is wise will accept his fate with the anger of a pachyderm, for it is best to die in battle. Not until we translate the death of one man into an exact quantum of energy of the universe can we be philosophers.

Since there is development instead of progress, why should we be astonished that we are of less use to clay, the bole, or to the turf than are willows or oaks, which can be converted into stone or sardonyx? Not far from the city of Coburg was a whole forest of agate. Either we are stone, or we are decayed wood which may never be transfigured into agate. It is idle and insane to complain against nature.

Strife and confusion haunt men until their death. The Greeks paid homage to a god of insolence; they brought votive offerings to Ceres, fear, and Eros. The Syrians on the Orontes showed the utmost veneration for an image of Fortune which Eutychides the sculptor had made for them. The earth has no need for the forceless; Acheron, the river of the dead, nurses white poplars, which Homer calls *Acherois*, for death is an absolute energy. The robber

Sisyphus is useful to destiny when dead, for he never ceases pushing the rock up to the mountainous peaks though it rolls down every time.

The season for sorrow, funerals, and the stubble in the wind is as regular as the time for nidification. One can count upon two to three hundred hogsheads of melancholia and waste every year before the Dog Star rises. What men ask for they harvest, for otherwise how could there be wars, ruin, and hatred? When men ate leaves and grass, they wept for the acorns of the *phlegos* oak. Then Pelasgus, the first king of Arcadia, gave them huts and pigskin shirts to protect them against rains and bogs, but mischance crept into their hovels and blouses; each one who prays to Zeus for gold, more acres, his neighbor's wife, is miserable enough to have his petition granted.

All is vanity and a striving after wind, and man has no profit of his labor except in his will. Lineage is our nemesis, foretelling our shames and how we shall go to the cerecloth. There is more bear's-foot in one brood than in another; bilberries settle on dry hillocks; toothwort sprouts beneath the hazel. What virtue is there in the crocus, which flowers in hard weather?

Olympias, mother of Alexander of Macedon, killed her husband and dragged his concubine Cleopatra and her infant son over a bronze vessel filled with fire, and Alexander himself slew ten thousand cities for no other cause but that his sire was Philip and that he was cribbed nine months in the belly of Olympias.

Have all the canticles, the thousands of poems, and the triremes that sang upon the rivers as swans betrayed us? Does knowledge make us base and killers? Cain was sent into the wilderness of Nod because he slew Abel, but each

169

who sorrows in the solitary forests has killed one who has called him brother.

Stones are for patience, but dust is in diverse places gathering rage and derision. Expired mountains suckle marble pillars; diorite is steadfast and starves the jackal. All the unguents of Astarte do not confuse Theban limestone; gall and the palmer worm cannot be mummified, and blood is no tablet for oaths. The corridors of the pyramids are dry of tears. Wicked Cheops in his tomb is a psalm; all else is rheum and water.

Lineage thrives beneath the limestone hills; the Nubian rock is the tablet of Cush. The kings of Sidon quarried their tombs in Egypt, and the steatite scarab remembers the Hyksos prince. Remembrance is petrified in rocks and stelae; angels are hieroglyphs cut into basalt ranges. Rains breed the wanton lizard and dissolve filial love; moisture is the substance of the spider. Sun and sphinx strike the maggot.

All annals are writ in equal dust. Adages are the worms in the sarcophagus; sin and love are mathematic in the tomb. Trees sicken, and dying flowers offend, though asphodels remain the same in the meads of the dead. What lives is sin and dross save it die, for there is no hurt in the winding sheets. Death attracts the valorous mind which is possessed by Atropos, who sends him to his end. The noblest heart perishes when it disburdens its destiny. The thinker lives solely to die: this is what Pascal calls the automatic need to finish: Abba, Abba, it is finished.

Quarry the blood as old debris and mound, for rubble and brick hide Rehoboth and Akkad, and ruin is the false morsel of fear and the grub. A body laden with Arabic mumia is a cure for our sloven days of shame and Sodom.

Can the shroud of Thothmes betray the maggot? Will the peristyle cower before Scythian Vulturnus? The pectoral set in the skeletal breast is obsidian, and papyrus is the vegetable raiment of queen Hentmehit; a senile column at Persepolis is the eagle's perch, while the parched gazelle sleeps on pylons in the dunes. Desert and skull prove the tooth of doubt; blood is king of waste, but relic and chagrin are sayings and lore.

Sepulchres are the archives of knowledge; they know most whose burial rites arouse awe. The ant inters the dead, and locusts, driven in great shoals by warm winds, expire with felicity in the marshes which were the abodes of the great Assyrian kings. The grave of Daniel lies at Shus. Nebbi Younis is the tomb of the prophet Jonah; may rocks shield him from his foe, the palmer worm. At Abydos the head of Osiris lies alone. Fence in the remains of Zephaniah with the sherd of Nineveh; the lamentation of Jeremiah is pyrite, may his tomb in Samaria never have a seam. Adam lies beneath the water meadows of Damascus. Oxhead is the cemetery of Alexander's charger; opposite the prison where Joseph deciphered the dreams of Pharaoh's baker and cupbearer was a vast graveyard of horses. Cato died in Utica, which is close by the greater Syrtis, where the lotus-eaters dwelt. We avoid being Cato by as short a distance as the gulf of the Lotophagi is from Utica.

Hew the slab fresh with grief from the mountain; the cave of Machpelah will keep Abraham entire. Lend not holy Isaac to the usurious worm. Oil of cedar protects the haunches of Phut; the body of Peter was laden with honey though the ink of Hermes was steeped in galls. Cyrus is a sage in his valley grave; noble and vain are the skulls of David and Isaiah. The sepulchres of Esther and Mordecai heal Ecbatna. Give a prayer for the detritus of deceased Heliopolis that contained the feet of Asenath, Joseph's bride. What sacral rubble holds the tunic of Moses? Is there yet a jamb or lintel Plato touched?

The jackal has no respect for the winding sheet, but all knowledge is in the tomb. The Andes is a necropolis of the mastodon, the monkey, and the jaguar, and there lies prehistoric man. The burial urn expels the mad Erinyes; papyrus does not moulder in the mummy pit, for barley and corn seed grow fat by dead Pharaohs. A dried pomegranate is as entire as the body of the prophet Samuel.

The earth is millions of years old, but it has not lost its wit or mind or virtue, for everything can be found in the ground. What man regards as recondite Sophia is the discovery of a humble seed, the use of an herb, or of an ass's skin. Empedokles blew up ass's bladders to catch the etesian gales.

Sun and moon are potsherds in the Valley of the Tombs; Rā and ancient Isis sleep among papyrus flowers. Apostle Thomas is interred in Edessa; may the smallest cumin seed cover his affection. King Tchesser is now a litter of Egyptian glyphs, for he hewed his woe in a channel of rock. Buttress all mortal works in calcareous stone, for even vilest Cambyses is an admonitory inscription. Granite sustains Baalpeor and the winged bull of Ashur. The rocks of Hetnub are steadfast sons. To betray is nature; fealty is in the grave. Keep the bones and boasts of Nimrod in gypsum; ignorance pours out the strength of awe. The honey of Babylon succors Alexander; the cerecloth of Amenhotep is the tunic of Osiris. Where are the remains of Magog and the river Goshen? The burial sites at Memphis can never be filled.

Steep the body of Jacob in mountain natron; Lazarus is moldy without the nard and drugs of Gaza; bitumen preserve the skeleton of Adam; cassia and myrrh guard the father's knees. Osiris is prudent in a hundred sacred tombs. Sorrow for the dead is an olden skill. The ancient gods taught Anubis embalming, and Hermes' sandals are shod by cobblers in Orcus; heed no sighs except the epitaph of stone. A thousand slabs are more prophetic than Tiresias, and the Holy Ghost can be contained in Adam's dust.

It is unreasonable to labor for posterity, and woeful to die, but natural; to do nothing is pernicious grief. Man works to remember, and a frugal headstone has more nature in it than a cenotaph.

There is rank superstition in Egypt's *Book of the Dead* and the worship of the cat, the dog, and the beetle and crocodile. Much of the ritual of the dead of ancient Egypt is a book of the dog, and Anubis, the great god, had this beast's head. At Mendes the goat was deified, and at Leontopolis the lion received duck, veal, honey, and groats, and all this is art and raging passion.

A remnant of the Cuthites journeyed to Iberia and built beacons or lighthouses of hewn rock which had one eye and were called Cyclopes. Cyclops is the progeny of Ham.

The cat is very dear to Ham, and the pyramids are abstract stone and marble desert cats. The Egyptians are a cat people, and the art of mummifying the deceased body is a feline art. The Egyptians despised shepherds, and Jacob's sons feared to tell Pharaoh that they were tenders of cattle. Wherever the heifer is scorned, the cat is holy; and where kine are sacral animals, as in the Vedic hymns and in Judaic law, the mouse, the kite, the eagle, and the cat are unclean.

When a dog died in the house of an Egyptian, he mourned and cast away all of his grain.

Ham was the first painter, for he cared more for his own image than for anybody. In ancient Israel Ham is an idol maker, and in Egypt Cush is an architect, and in Greek civilization Ham is called Narcissus. The greatest iniquity of Narcissus the artist is that he paints himself all day long; his canvases or stone idols are feminine toilet; for the ideal of Narcissus is the lavatory, the mirror, and the waste pipes which are known as esthetics. Ham, Cush, and Narcissus were the first plumbers. Narcissus makes the most intricate abstract drawings of cubes, triangles, and lozenges, which are nothing else but surrealist porcelain latrines; these are the idyllic canals for ordure in his intellect. He is a human bowel hater, and he is coprophagous, for he eats with his mind what the prophet Ezekiel in his zeal for fallen Israel would not. There has never been human excrement in the imagination of the Prophet. Ezekiel, to do penance for the sins of Israel, takes into his mind visions of cow ordure instead of human offal. A king in India always kept an ox at his side.

THE COST OF KNOWLEDGE is dear; the arts have not made men less vain than Absalom, nor less stupid than the Emperor Claudius, who added three letters to the Roman alphabet. One author of remote times declared that a good man is at one time good and at another bad, but he who fawns upon the Muses is more difficult to grasp than Proteus.

Though man is the only beast that can write, he has small reason to be proud of it. When he utters something that is wise it is nothing that the river horse does not know, and most of his creations are the result of accident. His celebrated songs fall out by chance and were not even known to him before he set them into meter. Poems are like worms, which, Aristotle says, come from snow that has lain a long time or originate in the dung of oxen and asses.

He who does not distrust art does not comprehend philosophy; but he who really cares for metaphysics loves Artemis, Apollo, and Endymion more than Pan. Apollo gave votive offerings to Dionysus before he followed Cybele in her wanderings to the blessed hyperborean's land. The vine is tender when man piously goes out to seek the earth. As long as the lamp of Pallas Minerva is filled and its flame never ceases to glow, man can pay homage to stones, stocks, and beasts. In Egypt a massebah was polished by the kisses of worshippers.

Neither Sparta nor Athens can be our mentor. The former produced no art, which made the Lacedaemonian so dour that it was a prodigy to see a Spartan smile. It takes a great deal of intelligence or naïve affection to smile well; neither Iago nor Polonius can do it; a good, honest laugh is a birthright, which the shrewd practice and the mediocre are unable to wear. Homer says that the Athenians were a dark-eyed, witty, and talkative people. All art is either the wagging of the tongue or of the shameful tail; a writer is an intellectual meddler. The Athenians were the greatest artists in the world; as Thucydides asserts, the men of Athens were born to trouble others.

Greece at the time paid vows to Athene and Artemis, who resembled handsome youths rather than maids. People are less surd to a doctrine or saying of a lewd urchin of Hellas than to one of Plato's, for this is not the age for the piety of George Herbert and the homilies of Izaak Walton, which will have to wait for another century or two to come from their ossuaries. We are ashamed of Anaxagoras, Theophrastus, and the semitic Thales and Eudoxus, and we cover them with darkness where all ignorance and vileness are hid: but in Paradise there is no night. At present, thinkers of antiquity appear to be more dead than the carcass of a mylodon, which is said to contain enough animal matter to give off a flame in a spirit lamp. La Fontaine believed that anyone who preferred his own time to that of the ancients was insane.

Truths and good books have the mold of a freshly dug grave and do not live again until some benign author has the power to say to them, "Come forth, Lazarus!" What booty is there in goodness and learning to the fierce, the expedient, and the world? We relish Homer, among other reasons, because Hera calls Artemis a "shameless bitch," and we would heed Paul's seventh chapter in *Romans* more did we know that he had lain with some hetaera in Greek Tarsus, where he was born. Tarsus is renowned because Cleopatra and Antony had an assignation there. Semiramis snares us more quickly than Paul because man is artistic rather than indignant.

Narcissus despoils the finest intellects of their fruits. No one can love his own image and care for philosophy. Writing is an exceptional vanity, and Solomon put down the fewest words because everything has been said. It is told that Diogenes wrote maybe no more than two dialogues or five at the most. People who hanker after originality are not only not to be trusted but are mad and ignorant. It would be best not to write at all except that people so readily forget what has been said. Worse, they despise oracles that are not brand-new so that a modern author with some skill in employing sentences feigns that he has the latest revelation from Jupiter or Orpheus. Despite long usage hallowed by Thoth and Hermes, some words are harshly scorned like good and evil, justice and virtue, and the only way to present such ideas anew is to show that the sages of Attica were not stale scholiasts or sciolists. It would be cant to describe Diogenes, Crates, and Zeno as saints, though they are sometimes referred to as the fathers of stoicism. They were secular savants for Diogenes asserted that cannibalism was good.

The brain is a poor reed shaken in every wind, and its fruits are the sport of dust. Solomon has said that the making of many books is a great weariness and that there is nothing new under the sun. There are no new books, and had men the least wisdom, they would read what has been written and use the Nile papyrus for shoes and raiment and not for more arrogant writings. It is of much doubt that the trade of letters has done anything else but whet greed and jealousy and hatred. Thoth has died, and the cicadas scorn the present alphabet men because they say they write for themselves although they are as gluttonous to be known as Tantalus in Erebus.

The sick have written astounding books: The poet Schiller was consumptive, and the odor of rotten apples quickened his soul; Hölderlin was insane; and Christopher Smart spent most of his latter days in Bedlam. Donne and Shakespeare, heretical bawds in their heyday, were broken in their fifties. Donne sat in his cerecloth for eight years. These men gave much to other people, and even to the universe, for unless man returns a tithe of what he has taken from nature, he is a skulking grout-head. But no one needs novel miseries, though some cultivate solitude, and most of our books look as though they were ill, lonely, and starved to death. Books should exhale affections, friendship, and good precepts and be redolent of the mulberry, osiers burning in the hearth, or lentils in the pot. The most pernicious volume is a cold one which is not conceived on Mount Ida but comes from the lawless lust of malignant privacies. Crates, seeing a young man walking by himself, said, "Have a care of lewd company." Men unaccustomed to people are savages and are as odorless as the eunuch.

The bad poet is a toady mimicking nature. Many poets and philosophers sat at the table of Dionysius the Tyrant; each one of them inclined his ear somewhat, as though this were the natural way of hearing, because Dionysius was rather deaf.

Dionysius could not refrain from writing tragedies, all of which were horrible. Nor could Plato abstain from visiting Dionysius. Is it credible that Plato expected a sensual carcass like Dionysius to give up his tyranny, which is the desire to rule everybody but one's self?

The good poet, as well as the philosopher, is the guardian and father of the races. Nicander in the *Georgics* is our mentor when he writes: "Terrible evils oftentimes arise from eating olives, or pomegranates, or from the trees of maple or of oak; but the worst of all are the swelling sticky lumps of mushrooms." Nicander also advises us that wild beetroot, sorrel, nettles, spinach, onions, and leeks should be boiled. It is remarkable that Heraclitus, often intemperately obscure and given to such abstractions as the logos, should have left among the smallest fragment of sayings the following: "Oxen are happy when they eat the bitter vetch."

The greatest poets teach many remarkable things, but poems give off a vapor like the tripod which clouds their meanings, and one is just as much gulled by Shakespeare as by a cutpurse, a liar, and an adulterer.

A poet ought not to trust himself, for he is a chameleon, assuming the complexion of his surroundings and has the slavish vices of his time. Pausanias, who displayed awe, which is a great gift, was foolish about the Pentathlon; he showed as much wonder for a statue of Symmachus, a wrestler, or for the inscription on a monument to Cleogenes, who had won a prize with a riding horse from his own stud, as he did for the Dioscuri or primeval Saturn. The maid Artemis grasps a lion in one hand and a leopard in the other, and this may seem to be superstitious and stupid, except to those who realize that only such ferocious beasts prevent men from violating the virgin. We must either judge or go mad; the reverence for the athlete in Pausanias or Pindar is base.

He who is least of all insane is the philosopher. The poet has a more prolific and winelike faculty and is the fountain in which the nurses of Bacchus were said to have washed him when he was born. Socrates was correct when he said that the poet could not explain his verses, for writing is sleep halved by dream—the dream is of a changing, watery substance. The prophetic life of Menelaus is spent on the Nile, grappling with Proteus, who is a river oracle.

Unless the poet goes each day to the Delphic sibyls or studies the oldest customs and laws of men, he is no better than a mime, or a stage singer. Without the aid of philosophy he is a flautist, and he loves only his windpipe.

There are no dogmas, there is only veneration and animal intimation. Pascal said that man is too stupid to invent a worm. He is also too ignorant to admit he is one. It is impossible for man to know anything, and utterly pusillanimous for him to cease striving after knowledge. The sage studies all the days of his vanity to make better mistakes.

The mullet hides his head, imagining he has concealed himself, which is the habit of the mediocre.

The last works of thinkers are sometimes alluded to as their senilia, but this does not mean that these are feeble cries but that they are the fabled songs of death the swan utters in her final throes. The swan is fierce, and no poet hears the hymn of this dying bird without cosmical trembling, and there is as much courage in the swan in its last moments as in Plato's *Laws* written at seventy-five. A story exists that Socrates had a dream of a cygnet and that the next day Plato came to see him. Helen was born from a bird, the offspring of Leda and Zeus, who took the shape of a swan, and she was a great beauty and did as much mischief as divine Plato. As Callimachus held, a great book is a great evil. There is as much malice in genius as good.

No one really invents anything; Homer sings what he has compiled, and he creates neither Ilium, Menelaus, nor Agamemnon but catalogues their deeds in a cadence, for Orpheus and Apollo and Pan are the sweet sounds that come out of pipes, reeds, and flutes; but it is said that Apollo laid aside the lyre to follow Cybele, which means that the earth is more sacred than music. In the ground are the annals of the many leafy races that perish, and Homer, like Apollo, gathers these records which Cybele has in her bosom. Homer had a moral ear rather than merely a pipe or flute.

Plato said that music enslaved the multitude, and people listen to the most consummate sounds either lying on sofas or their faces cast into such rapturous vacancies that it is hard to know whether they have the groaning sleep of a sow or a stygian ecstasy. In this humbug mood of intellectual attention they assume the posture of a disgusting lick-spittle or one of the dwarfs of Domitian. Apollo flayed Marsyas and hung up his skin in a cave because he was a loutish flautist. Piping is a stupid, gossipy art which has spoiled whole countries.

Strabo tells us that the elephants of India could be taught to obey by words and that others were pacified by tunes accompanied with the beating of a drum. Unfortunately, music either puts the mind to sleep or inflames men. Though everyone regards music as a good power, it is often a malefic one, and poets who are more concerned with the ear than with the moral intellect are harmful. Anacreon of Teos was a wine sieve, and much of his poetry was written to praise the tyrant Polycrates.

Most of the *Iliad* is taken up with the war at Troy; many for this reason have thought Homer to be a martial poet, which is untrue. Strife is the god which destroys those who crouch before destiny. Homer readies the soul for fate, and Hesiod prepares it for frugality. Zeus sends penury to man, declared Hesiod, and he who has never laid the osier and the penny fruits and seeds at the altar of indigence has a sluggish ear for the sorrows of the needy.

Man studies philosophy to resist pleasure or reads poetry that he may not grow crabbed or morbid. When Porphyry conversed with his pupils, they often drank wine though he never took any. It is told that Alypius, living about the same time, was almost a pigmy in stature and that he was well-nigh all soul and intelligence, his body being too small for corrupt matter to forage or pasture there. Man at present is far less soul than body; he is hurt in all places, and he walks on his wounds, and this is his pleasure, his pain, and his art. He is not as carnal as he thinks; for though, as Catullus says, he perambulates all beds as though he were the white doves of Zeus, this is the songless, exhausted century. The virgins have gone, chaste Diana has departed, and O Catullus, where are the unblemished youths? Who supplicates Priapus for his powers, or pours out libations to Poseidon? In the *Rig-Veda* man is told not to utter a mundane thought in the morning.

VI

MORE TOWNS AND CITIES are destroyed by sexual disorders than by plagues, famine, and disease. Unless men follow some discipline, they are demented from birth until their demise. Numa Pompilius, seeing how fierce the people had grown because they were always at war, built the fane of Janus, which was open when the cities of Latium were in arms and shut when they were quiet. Numa appointed days for feast and rest, which are called the *fasti*; he divided the year into twelve moons, or months. He paid homage to Jupiter, as the cosmos is sacred, and he did not omit war or chastity, for when men fail to canonize their lusts, they are most brutal. Besides, reverence for the planets and for vestals keeps men still a little while.

Man is not by nature ascetic or domestic; the human anthropoid would be a house dove eating the mast and roosting in the beeches were he not wild. Cyclops is a steadfast eater of men; the rough Solymi are incessantly arrogant; Ares or a javelin is the deity of Magog. It is the irregular outbreaks of passions that are unexpected despots we seldom overwhelm. The fool is wet and parched, beckons one from whom he flees, and is cloyed all in one hour. The hardest man to endure is one's self, and he is the most untrustworthy of foes. If one wears the livery of the meek, he creeps too low, or when one cries out, "My God, I am a gnat," he dilates his throat; the recluse complains because the daughters of Judah do not come to gladden him.

Scylla is a fit of passion which men must try to avoid, as we should endeavor to shun every tumid emotion, wrath, libidinous visions, cupidity, vanity, self-love. Anthisthenes was reported to have said that, if the wise man does anything, he does it in accordance with virtue as a whole.

It is much more difficult to eschew the passions that resemble snow rather than fire. Men with the fewest words break out on a sudden, and without cause, and like Ajax mistake the sheep for Agamemnon, or as Achilles go into combat with the River Scamander. Achilles, whose mother, Thetis, is hoary sea water, has cold wrath.

Man is the most confused beast in the earth; he marvels at the twelve houses of lust Tiberias built at Capri and is unable to abhor Heliogabalus, who kept the snows of Armenia in diverse caves to cool his debauched Roman blankets. Alexander was embalmed in honey, and so are all his acts, because men care more for prodigies than they do for the wise or the just.

Men crave to be plants, shrubs, bog moss because their hearts cry out for quiet; a species of pecten which has no offal would have been Dr. Swift's Elysian morsel. The ordinary man dungs upon his spirit, and there is no niter to cleanse him. Chagrin is the honey and the teacher; never to fail is a ditch and delusion and to go all one's days in the same debauched livery. We endeavor to be abstemious, or never slough a single folly. In Crete there was a plane which never lost its leaves because Zeus lay with Europa under this tree; vice is constant and ripens with age; old mulled sins are the worst; he who has never shed the leaves of his youth is always stupid.

Without genitals or indifferent ones, man is neither rock nor water. Parmenides denied the existence of motion, which is Eros, for whenever men move, they stir up the blood. Augustus required his wife, Livia, to procure women for him because it was too painful for him on occasion not to discharge his inflamed vessels.

Man is more ill-made than are the quadrupeds in many respects. Goaded sorely and torn by his appetites, he envies the goat, who is able to have sexual intercourse all his life. He has the utmost desire to abstain from venery so long as he is capable of enjoying it. Origen deliberately became a *spado* because he knew that, as long as man is tormented by that wallet of shame, he will lie and cozen and scratch himself. Sophocles in his old age had said that he was grateful that that riotous, unruly member no longer bothered him.

Seneca was of the mind that the groans and ejaculations that men fear and tremble for are in themselves trivial and

186

contemptible. Not everyone is Demitris the Cynic, who was said by his adversaries to practice mortification. Epicurus, whose name has come to stand for hedonism, took his sickness as a philosophic discipline, and though he died of the agony of the stone, he expired blessing his fate.

There is no doubt that the sensual is very attractive, and it would be wrong not to set before the reader Lais of Corinth and the Pramnian wine. One cannot hide the pears, the fair Corinthian girls, and hope to inculcate in men a valorous continence by a species of skulking and stealth as if virtue could be taught by robbing men. Everybody has to choose, and one will honor neither a man who abstains from a lust of which he has no knowledge nor a teacher who feigns that pleasure does not exist.

There is much difference between the disgraces of the hot man and the wether, unless the latter has brought this upon himself for virtuous purposes, or nature has made him mild. The neuter has no earth in his faculties or flesh and no innocence; Ovid identified Vesta with the hearth. When Agrippina prepared to poison Claudius, she asked Locusta to make up the decoction but Halotus the eunuch to administer it.

Many of the Sophists were moral teachers who grew more stoical but not after their powers had flagged. What is the good of being Solomon or Aristotle and composing *Ecclesiastes* or the *Metaphysics* if one turns his face to the wall because his penis was not erect in the presence of a chit? If man can make the wisest philosophy and have no satisfaction of it because the pudendum is faithless, then all is lost, and man has no other choice but to be a sparrow or a newt. Nobody recollects pleasure except dimly, for one can remember the shape of a cube or an isoceles triangle but not the color of the nipples of Daphne nor the aches she once gave us.

Asceticism has always attracted the most carnivorous and sexual men. The Socratic head looked like neither the beautiful cranium of Apollo nor that of Buddha. Socrates was a thick-looking man, with the heavy mouth of an orgiast and ugly as Thersites. Want, Poverty and Philosophy are such sages that those who follow these three are often better than men who appear to have the self-abnegating mien. Penury is an accursed blessing, according to Langland's Piers the Plowman.

The young should be nurtured in Sparta, and they should be taught to pray very often, for the navel is no more than the span of a palm from the shameful organ. A rude and hard infancy, according to Balzac, is best for the development of character. Eros is wily, feigning that the whole of human existence can be contained in the table, stool, and bed.

There are many things to be said for the bed provided one does not lie in it all day long; though Zeus could do it with impunity, man cannot. Besides, if a man is not a foolhardy sensualist, he is not likely to weaken the members he so covets that by forty they are a pendulous memorial of quondam pleasures.

"But in every case we must be most upon our guard against what is pleasant, and pleasure," Aristotle writes. Plato said that extreme pleasures and pains produce madness. Delights make men rave. No one knows anything and can only surmise that his knowledge is an ethereal zero. Were it not so, men would be more overweening than they are.

The men that are most interesting are those who have

valiantly resisted the delights for which they ached. Solomon said, "Do not give all your strength to women," which is wise. One does not go to genius to be one of the cripples or the blind at Bethesda, but to be healed and to be seamed together again. The Essenes were craftsmen and healers, and the word means to cure. Luke was also a physician. It is best not to abjure the fruits of the earth if this makes one irascible. A philosopher is a vestal when he rejects what hotly draws him, for the best of men are not those who abstain because they have no testicles but those who attempt to govern that Aetna between their legs. No matter what sage or philosopher or poet we cite, we have to return to the same vexing dilemma: Should man copulate?

It is hard to be Socrates when one has capital testicles, and only a plagiary of virtue if one has not. Who can brag the goodness of a dead phallus? And what bravery is there in the abstemiousness of a man who has a worthless prepuce? Moreover, it is redundant to be temperate when one is already impotent. What is overcome is good, for man has a negative conscience—the monitor or daemon in Socrates which prevented him from doing wrong, but did not compel him to perform what is right.

Evil, which is our companion all our days, is not to be treated as a foe. It is wrong to cocker vice, but we grow narrow and pithless if we are furtive about it, for this is at best a pretense, and the sage knows good and evil are kindred. The worst of men harm others, and the best injure themselves.

Man is always tempted, and it is what he avoids rather than what he does that enobles his character; the Crees knotted a few willow bushes together, which represented their deity, Kepoochikawn. This is a very rude image of

189

divinity, but less woe and vanity will come of it than from the Zeus of Praxiteles or the temple of Solomon. Cree warriors ate live coals to be gods, and when they suffered pains, drums were beat so that their groans would not be heard.

It is possible to overvalue the ascetic habits, and many will complain that the beast's skin and club of Hercules, Stoic symbol of principles and frugality, are not sufficient for human wit or manners. This is very likely so, and even Seneca, living in the midst of the turpitudes of Nero, said, "I am not yet come to my own frugality." There is much confusion abroad, and our poets are no wiser than the street urchin. This, of course, Plato discerned, and many blame him for setting up a severe fratery, yet there is no man who is not a far greater despot to himself than he believes the laws of Plato's *Republic* to be.

Here is a riddle: If the gospel and many wise books have been written to govern the genitals and to take away the imperial mind from this rugose wallet of mirth, how is it that a boy just growing his pubes and while at chapel, and without the least thought of anything save Mark and Luke, has an erection? This is as much of an enigma as the Ephesian sod, and must be considered along with the lilies and the *Proverbs of Solomon*.

VII

MAN HAS NO positive abiding tenets; his genius is negative, the Socratic *elenchus*, which urges him not to be unjust, intemperate, self-loving, and covetous. "All our errors," said Rochefoucauld, "come from self-flattery." Human skin has no greater wish than to lie among the water lilies and to forget. Lechery enters the understanding heart, for no one can eat of the Tree of Knowledge and be innocent. Images make us cunning and unreliable, but without them we are brutes and stones. The primitive Pelasgians had no knowledge of figures, and they set up unwrought rocks to represent Cronus and Hera, and were natural.

Confucius said that, when people prate much of virtue,

there is none, and when they talk too much of the family, it has decayed, and when they are continually babbling about their homeland, they have already cursed the earth. The most barbaric nations that guarded their countries with shields made out of the skin of the riverhorse cared more for their hearth and wives than does the present anthropoid.

People have almost no will to be simple; the most acute rapture is in being roundabout. The tanner and the potter were in the mind of Socrates when he uttered a precept, and the market place was his fane. Paul's head was thrown into a sheepfold, and the brother of Jesus was killed by the pole of a fuller. The saint's pericranium lies among the lambs; heaven bless the sheep pen and preserve the fuller, lest Paul and James be forgot.

Man is a vast riddle to the gentle heart until he comes to the desolate conclusion that he can do no better than he does. Captain John Smith, who settled the Virginia Plantation, said that his greatest disease was his endeavor to do good. This is a precious malady, and each one should do all he can so to sicken, but he must never forget that he is ailing of virtue.

Yet man remains untamed, and the human being can never gratify his mouth, arms, hands, or feet. His passions are as mixed as the cameleopard or the hippocentaur. The chimera, the unicorn, the harpy, the griffin are different aspects of his chaotic nature. Can one fathom such a creature who is a quadruped, reptile, insect, and bird? He is never of a single brood or tribe. The Achlis who sleeps leaning against a tree arouses envy in him simply because he goes to bed. He will hurry more quickly to starwort or marsh rushes, if he has never eaten them, than to the wild ases relished by Phoebus Apollo. He craves every novelty and is for that reason continually a bane to himself and a surprise to others. Man runs to the lizard, which he is told is an aphrodisiac, although his prostate is already worn out and he is suffering from urinary retention. When informed that in India elephant tusks are used instead of gates, he is rapturous. The ordinary bores him; he reviles the season, the turtle rains, the April leaves which bring him no havoc, nor happiness. God created the day to dispel the void which is the delirium of man.

Nobody is quiet, for tedium is every man's gibbet; ennui makes men pilfer themselves of friends and sack their hopes or the good luck singing in their pockets. Rest in people is unbearable; we are the white malms the frosts and rains crumble into the manure with which we dress our pasture. Man is a bore four seasons of the year, and stupid every day. His character is seldom awake at dawn. Sleep is a coward's mire, and each day is another Circe's sty of inertia.

Almost all trouble comes from impatience. We burn with satiety, which has a use also, for Naples is paved with the lava of Scala. The greatest sorrow is that one believes either there is free will or that there is absolutely none. Not to do anything is an offense against nature, which is always energetic. There is no battle man can wage that is so essential to his intellect as the war against necessity.

Fate turns aside from the lethargic; the Lord of the Psalmist, who breaks the ships of Tarshish with an east wind, is Himself impaired by the sluggard. Man's might is piddling, but the ground hungers for it.

People throw away their heritage and even their lives for no other cause but impatience. We are the meacocks of a grubby destiny because we cannot wait. There are months which are as chaff in the wind, and all our labor is lost. When the long rains settle in the head and the cliffs and headlands within us are covered with fog, we cannot hear Homer.

The ring ouzel winters in mountainous countries; hedgehogs make their hibernacula with leaves and moss, and hempseed contents the swallow. But will apples comfort the heart or the flagons of Cana wine stay ennui? There is no trident to sweep the tides of the soul or univalve in which to catch its surging beat. Virtue often has the ague; the spleen in talent is damaging Danewort.

The affections of human beings are a weather-cock and are turned one way or another by mischance and sickness. Many signs are given to us to indicate that we are rejected; the Latins referred to every door as Janua, and though we know, without thinking, when this door is open or shut, we attempt to pass through it at all times. People give off an intellectual effluvium which draws or chokes us. The vine cannot endure the smell of the cabbage; ivy stifles the oak.

Man falls out with one he loves, discovering that his fresh adversary has canine teeth and that she had smiled too warily to have shown them earlier. After we have ceased to look upon the beloved with hot or inflamed eyes, little that is not gall or dross remains of the quondam inamorata. We remember that her nostrils were puerile and that her mouth was the ejected stomach of a fish when pursuing prey. Only when the affections ebb, do we see the flats and the rubble our tidal emotions had covered; often what looks sloughy and fruitless is our own vacant hearts.

Who can say to his soul, I did not recognize the liar and the thief who took my green herbs and laid waste my furze and haws. Everyone must give himself up to some thought,

194

vision, or *ultima Thule*, or else live torpid and disgrace the
ground he treads. It is more important to be a dupe than to
be Timon; a man who cannot be deceived is shrewd, which
is icy insanity.

Still, the gull enlarges his vices no less than the deceived.
He who is not a hunter is the prey. The lurcher ambushes
the fallow deer, and each one satisfies the other, because the
captive is as ready to be taken as was Theodota the
courtesan.

We are not often ready for our friends; some wait for the
setting of the Pleiades to give their affections, or say they
will act upon knowledge later, which is stomach thinking.
The maudlin bask in easy, vernal raptures, which they consider ideas or emotions, but are wind eggs called *zephyria*,
birds lay these barren eggs when the soft breezes stroke
their feathers. Man hunts the faults of his companions when
tedium inflames him, for when nothing happens to man, he
looks for disaster, a flood, a hurricane, the death of a loved
one; his stupor is gratified by newspapers, the water-closet
obsequies of the rout. Men would not require earthquakes,
fires, funerals to instruct them were they born wise, for each
one has all these tumults within him. But some are of a
froward temperament and look to such miserable accidents
as fresh experiences. Heraclitus held that war is the father
of progress; pain is a deity, a Buddha, or a devil. So long as
man is as malformed as he is, he will kill and torment and
seek the wheel, the rack, and the scaffold as a remarkable
sensation. Affliction is more important to mortals than Ionic
luxury, and ill hap is food for the sluggard. The Shulamite
of Solomon is the smallest of gratifications to the human
biped. Myrrh and unguents and all the spices of Arabia
Felix are not enough for him. Mortification and crucifixions

draw him greatly. Lucretius asserted that human beings derive unusual felicity from seeing people drown. Each one is relieved because he is not dying, but he also trembles with subtle joy at the sight of the pyre, seeing a man castrated, or witnessing violence.

Many think solitude marvelous though the cemeteries are filled with such contented corpses. Loneliness is the ecstasy of the humbug, for everybody is as alone as he wants to be. The shroud will wrap us up soon enough without hankering after the satisfactions of the shades.

Most men require stern gods if they are not to run mad and be thieves; the stone boundaries were regarded as divinities, and no one dared defile a rock that separated his farm from his neighbor's. These deities or stones which separate one man's property and another's should be well defined in friendship. People should regulate their friendships, for though it melts the heart to sighs and clouds when a companion hastens to our relief, it is better not to expect it. A savant recognizes a foe, a demigod a false friend. A real friend is a doughty warrior, a Hector, who is described by Aeschylus as having a heart softer than a mulberry. There are certain burdens we must keep to ourselves, first of all our lamentations. Few can endure another man's misfortune and sit down with him in his plight and sadly eat together the walnuts of Zeus or rest beneath the beech trees, which Nicander, in the *Georgics*, says are the altars of Pan.

Pindar claims that fortune is one of the Fates; character and misfortune are the same mineral. Each one has title and deed to his miseries. "The ox knoweth his owner, and the ass his master's crib"; the unfortunate sits upon his evil luck until it is hatched.

A Greek Cynic said that one should be prepared to detest

a friend because it was almost certain that he would be a foe. The erudite is no more fervent than the weather-headed fellow. Humble people accept their limitations more quietly and without the vanity of those who are talented. Pedants suppose that the mind is a divinity, but it is less sure than the foot. One knows with some assurance where the foot will go, provided the mind is not guiding it.

People do more to earn a disadvantage than to purchase a benefit. Those who hanker after friends either hawk round them as though they were their prey or, disappointed, mew themselves up in a room called society. A disorderly biped, man is as sloven in his discontent as he is in his pleasant, leafy summers. The blackthorn blossoms when a cold northeastern wind rears its branches; the sand martins lie torpid and without food amidst their *latebrae* until the sun beckons them again.

Fragrant skin fetches the hypocrite and the fleshmonger. We invite flesh, pleasant underwear, costly socks to our homes; the guest in the house of the Pharisee spreads the odor of myrrh, cassia, and Arabian balsam, though aromatic plants flee from hard weather. The wild olive at Olympia is one of the most perdurable trees, but this is the fruit of Pallas Athene who is wisdom. Does one ever find out who is a pond, desert, or ocean shrub? Moonflower, goat willow, duckweed are lake plants; botany gives us assurances which men do not. Can one guess who is loyal? Suffering Job is eaten up by his friends.

Men are more jealous than birds or quadrupeds because they are the prisoners of revenge and envy. Even the Greek soothsayers were covetous. Calchas died of vexation because Mopsus was a better prophet than he was.

Man is most easily wounded because he mistakes an asp or

fox for a friend. It is simpler for Hercules to carry out the dung from the Augean stables than to cast out the bile of an antagonist. Livia detested Germanicus for no other reason except that her joints were old and rancid and filled with spleen whilst he was modest and young. This hapless prince had earned the vilest thoughts from his brother, whom he had aided and never harmed.

Germanicus had a gentle disposition, but his brother was rapacious Tiberius, and his grandmother, the malevolent Livia. Tiberias practiced every cunning, so that his liberal acts made him an impostor among the Romans. The Parthians despised him for having a sluggish interest in horses, in the chase, and because the humblest subject could see him without much hindrance.

Piso was another viper among the hedges who awaited the death of Germanicus. Nature was tardy in satisfying Piso. What he could not accomplish by poison he expected to gain by spells and the effect of baleful portents upon the fevered mind and body of Germanicus. Piso commanded his lictors to bring exhumed corpses upon which were inscribed the name of Germanicus into the room where the prince was confined; should his vitality not be squandered by the disease, then theses evil omens would attack his reason and madness would force him to quit this life.

The lion and the eagle and the crocodile are not the peers of Tiberius, Livia, or Piso. The male crocodiles kill each other to possess the female, who shows a considerable attachment for her young. The lion is malicious when his teeth are anile, because he is no longer vigorous enough to attack any one as effectively as man.

Tired men are the most perfidious; the weak are foul enemies and dissemblers whose canorous words about the

198

good and the true are the covert for their corruption. Always infants in vileness and abominations which never grow any taller, for yea, they are the sucklings out of whose mouths come the innocent filths.

Man seldom relinquishes a single fault he condemns in others; for he is deaf to a rebuke. He covets what he does not want; alas, the bread he casts upon the water is returned to him. Most of the time is given to improving his vices; he cannot bear to be taken for a simpleton in the game of malice. When the viper is unable to poison his victim, he fetches his whole brood to pour out their venom with more success. When the fangs are not shown at once, we do not know where they are; the teeth of the polypus are between her feet.

It is told that, when a viper eats a scorpion, its bite is fatal; whether true or not, this is enough to cause the guileless to hide and the wicked to kill. There is no remedy for deceit or venom. Aristotle tells of the plant silphium, in which nests a serpent whose spittle destroys life unless one takes a small stone out of the tomb of an ancient king and pounds and mixes it in wine and drinks it. The stone is supposed to be asafetida, but this is a fable, for there is no decoction in the tomb or anywhere else to cure one of the serpent's bile.

Men of earth and water are sundered and perplexed. Fish and man are Dagon, the obelisk is Baal. The Tree of Knowledge is the accursed Serpent, and he who eats of it will creep in the dust forever; his head shall not be honest with his foot, and his hands shall be both the cherub and the raven; his tongue shall be confusion, fox, and shame; he shall be as Balaam, who flogged the ass that saw the angel. Mischance and the vulture are constant, but pleasant tidings drink up the pity in mortals.

199

VIII

THE AMERICAN IS a treeless ghost. Without ocean or ground, he raves for sea salt and cries out for the palms. The forests howl in the human brute; his arms and feet languish for want of clay and gravel; what can quiet this houseless spirit?

Man is the loneliest worm, and there is no spider or reptile so desolate as Aristotle's forlorn featherless biped. Porpoises sport in pairs, dolphins swim together in the Amazon and in the shoaly water at the mouth of the Tocantins. The *Midas argentatus* frolic with one another along the cacao branches.

But no beast is as placeless as the human being; the ouakari monkeys are found only on the banks of the Japura; taken from their native woods, they grow peevish and die of a lung disorder. The Juris and Passés perish of consumption after the least contact with the treeless white man.

One's origins matter most. Strangers are crazy to be indigenous; what soil or clime is their aliment they do not know. The mud of wells produces the ascarides; palms dote on salt, and fishermen anoint the holes of rocks to catch the Testacea which live in them. The Gospel of Matthew is impregnated with the salt of coastal Judea. Christ is the fish, Pisces, the salt-water star. Mud, fuci, saline quagmire satisfy some minds. Once men forsake their sources, a race of deceivers is spawned.

Men are beggars in desolation. Overwhelmed by sorrow or need, they reveal their beginnings. Do we learn what element prevails within us, whether we are a range of hills, and when we are at flood tide? Denials are our half-wild cattle in the mighty Amazon which drown, starve, or are the booty of the alligators. No one can go beyond the confines of himself.

A river has an entire identity which a Ptolemy or a Juba can know, and at its source it is mild and can be forded; man is marl, a sandy campo, and he is broken into many fragments by his sundry inceptions. Indians on the banks of the Japura fall ill when the Solimões breathes the detritus of their clay and vegetable mold upon them.

The white man is a captive of the new continent, according to William Carlos Williams, the only poet with the historian's faculty of the American earth. The beginnings of the American are a Babel to himself. A stranger in the earth, he exudes the sullen weather of New York, which has no dry heat or austere winter. The North American Caliban, neither hot nor cold, cannot attach himself to his neighbor;

and solitude is fatal to the affections. The Canadian Indians, after losing their kindred, tore up their tents, destroyed their possessions, and wailed together.

The treeless paleface cannot come to the ground; the mountains do not know him, and the mesa has forgotten him. Few and meager are the legends in the new land. The naturalist has called a tree of Brazil the *Cecropia*, which is the food of the sloth. This serpent tree, for the ancient Cecrops was a human snake, nourishes the sloven.

The *Pelopaeus* wasp has working songs, one when he carries the clay in his mandibles and another after this labor is done. What chant is there for drudgery in North America? Who molts his infamy or flowers: June and July leaf the campos; can tedium produce seeds for herons and storks?

The vampire bat devours the acajous and guavas, but the table of North America is sick. The songless hands of its natives are rude in amours; they have no time to savor the bride and to faint with love for her flesh and her delicate garments. The wings of the greenfinch are wounded when hungry for mating, and the cock snipe and windhover languish.

Impotency is growing apace in the New World, and the womb is barren. Without progeny the male is a grub; childless wedlock is the earthen jar which can never be filled with the Cana wine. Turtles, unable to hatch their eggs, scatter them in despair over the swamps.

Indian women strew their clothes with the feathers of the uirapara as a philtre. Anoint the fingers with mandragora; Leah's teats are starveling fruits, and her belly as seedless as the orchard graft, the stoneless grape, and the hybrid orange. God return the natural vintage and the citrous branch of Mesopotamia and Brazil.

We waver between equatorial weather and the poles; the moral man is as amphibious as the asphodel or the squill, land and sea plants. The irresolute long to winter on a Canadian bog covered with willows, larch, and spruce. The rich muse upon paintings of Eskimo sails made of whale gut, but this is the sleep whose seeds are scattered in dry ravines.

People in the new continent have no constant temperature or nature because they are placeless; transplanted persons suffer most from the disease of moroseness. The Indian, a cleft Tartar, sickens easily in moist Brazil.

Boys in America, often gentle before coming into their *virilia*, grow fierce and sullen within two to three years. Indians with a tractable disposition disappear after puberty, spending the rest of their lives in the *sertão* or by the banks of feral rivers. Trees depend upon the sites rather than their fruits or seeds to sire good progeny. The ash or poplar, and the olive on Parnassus, are the hardiest; mountain or forest wood is least corrupt. The seeds of sweet pomegranate produce a depraved tree. The sorb is sterile if removed to a warm vale; it is alleged that water snakes change into vipers when the marshes are parched.

Wild people ripen late and seldom bear fruit. The North American is a cold, hilly race; in his beginnings he had a snowy vigor; Thoreau, Whitman, and Melville are Olympian trees, half-cultivated but doughty. The cypress grows on Mount Ida, the terebinth springs up on rough Syrian slopes; silver fir, the valonia oak, and the kermes oak seek their home on the flanks of ranges.

Oak and plane have deep roots; the trees of pleasure, olive and pomegranate, shallow ones. Papyrus makes men vainglorious, and it grows in the shoals. Hardihood and loyal traits repel the comfortable; mountain trees are sturdy and rough; lakes are congenial, indolent friends, but they do not enliven us. People use each other, which nature and love allow. The toady drains his benefactor, the lover dilates his force. Human beings and nations are no different from insects and trees.

The Quiché Maya Codex is jaguar psalms. Aztec hieroglyphs are water demons and the human skulls sacrificed in the oratories. Thoreau's precepts are the strongest books of the American smell of the slime, the horny spicules of sponges, and the spermaceti of leviathan.

IX

MEN TRAVEL in search of strange hemispheres, little suspecting that they are ransacking their origins. Doom was the loot of the conquerer; he gathered ruin, misfortune, and death. We are so astonished by men gorged with the calamities of the world that knowledge of their rueful pilgrimage gives us pleasure rather than sorrow.

Juan Ponce de León came to the American coast on Easter and, with what thoughts he had of the lilies of Christ or of Prosperine can only be guessed, called the land *Florida*, or the coming up of flowers. In 1521 Ponce de León returned to Florida, and landing, he received a mortal wound in the thigh and died a few days later in Cuba.

Francisco de Córdoba arrived with one hundred Spaniards, and in sore need of water went ashore; one drank until he was bloated and died; other soldiers were killed by Indians; Córdoba died from wounds shortly after his return to Hispaniola.

In 1521 Lucas Vásquez de Ayllón set out in two vessels for the mainland, looking for the man-eating Caribs to work in the mines of the Antilles. He saw cultivated pearls, which shook his reason. No one can see what the albatross eats, and avaricious Christians have no less skill than this carrion feeder. Reaching the province of Chicora, he went inland, where he saw very white Indian giants. By a ruse he got one hundred and thirty Indians to board his ships and then set sail for Hispaniola. But almost all the natives perished, sorrowing for their wives and children and maize fields.

Lucas Vásquez set out a second time for the continent of Florida, and took his pilot Miruelo. Unable to find Chicora, the pilot succumbed to the watery fever known as melancholy, and died insane.

Vásquez again came to Florida in 1524. He despatched two hundred of his Spaniards to a village not more than a league from the Florida coast, and the Indians received the Spanish soldiers with great affection, feasting them for four days; and when their guests were glutted with maize, fish, and meat, they killed them.

Pánfilo de Narváez, the *adelantado* of Florida, left San Lucar with five vessels, and six hundred men to pacify Florida to the Rio de los Palmas. When he arrived at Hispaniola, only one hundred and eighty men were alive. After procuring more men and supplies in Cuba, he sailed to the Bay of Santa Cruz with three hundred men and forty-two horses; shortly after one vessel was lost on the fierce coast.

From the beginning, Narváez's men were scathed by the sea and the tempests, which blew continually into their heads and bowels. After one storm they found the small boat of a ship in the branches of a tree and sixty dead Spaniards with faces raveled and distorted from beating against the rocks. The trees were riven and prone, the earth sour and sere, and the grass and the leaf were slain by sea salt and the black angelic winds.

Pánfilo Narváez had been told by the Indians there were gold and silver in Apalaché; the three hundred Spaniards led by Narváez walked in bitter sea water to Apalaché, which was in northwestern Florida and extends from Pensacola to the Ocilla River. With nothing to eat but two pounds of biscuit and a half a pound of bacon, as an allowance for fifteen days, they were as dejected as the forty-two horses that had survived the Florida gales. But they were still callow in the pangs of woe.

They came to the Suwannee River, whose violent and sinister current took hold of a Spaniard and his horse, drowning both of them. The men grieved over their companion, but the horse they ate for supper that night.

At Apalaché there was dry maize, and forty low huts of thatch surrounded by forests, lagoons, and fenny ground. Cedar, evergreen oak, savin, the palmetto, and the alligator tree were abundant. There were deer, hares, lions, and a small brute with a pouch on its belly, besides night herons, partridges, merlins, sparrow hawks, mallards, and gerfalcons. The Indians went naked, were well-made of body, and had arrows, thick as the arm, which they shot with precision. There were forest, quagmire, and mountain cat, with beans and pumpkins in the fields, but no Patagonian ore. In place of gold and silver they saw raw, wooden mortars in which maize was cracked; it was a nine days journey on foot through lagoon water reaching up to the paps to come to the pumpkins, maize, and beans of Auté.

Pánfilo Narváez was in so doleful a condition, his hopes weaker than his legs, that he asked his men how they could retire from earth so malign. The Spaniards repaired to a water of sorrows they called the Bay of Horses. Here they wept and slew the poor brutes they had to eat. Without tools, iron, or forge, they made pipes out of wood which with deer skins they shaped into bellows; stirrups, spurs, and crossbows were cut and beaten into nails, saws, and axes. They had resolved to quit the land in five barges, which had to be built. The boats were calked with the fiber of the dwarf palm; rope and rigging came from horses' tails and manes. The savins provided the oars. There was scarce any rock for ballast or anchor, and no mountains to strengthen their will. The country was morass, without hills or summits foaled by Ocean. A sterile lava peak gems the mind, for in Scoriae amber grows.

They flayed the legs of the horses, using the skins for water bottles. They foraged for shellfish in coves and creeks, but forty died of hunger; others were ambushed by the naked giant archers in the reeds.

There is the Maya goddess of suicide, Ixcab, who is the patroness of men hindered by evil stars. The Spaniards, kindled by ruin, had no such deity, and none did harm to themselves. Some found shellfish, and the Indians killed ten who were digging in ravines or in creeks for food. In the haven at the Bay of Horses there were dried mullet and roses, which relieved them. The bottles made out of the horses' legs rotted, and they were without water for five days. A few swallowed sea salt, and three or four died crazy. The storm never stopped, blowing and beating them into twisted, gaunt skin. At Pensacola Bay a canoe of Indians was sighted. When they visited these natives, they found clay jars of water and a pile of dried fish set outside the savage hovels. The cacique gave them fish and water, and the Spaniards brought them the maize they had, and they ate in one another's presence. At midnight the Indians fell upon the sleeping Spaniards, massacring as many as they could.

Setting sail in their barges, they entered an estuary and saw other Indians in a canoe, who wore their hair long and loose and were robed in martens, heavy with musk.

Cabeza de Vaca, in the first boat, came upon the great waters of the Mississippi, which De Soto saw fourteen years later. To the Spaniards it was *Espiritu Sancto,* or the River of the Holy Ghost; the priest Marquette called it *Concepción.* The great river was as holy to La Salle and Joutel as the map of the earth was to Ptolemy. Cabeza de Vaca was treasurer and high sheriff of the Narváez expedition and a grandson of the conqueror of the Grand Canary. His fable is wilder and more epic than the twenty years of sorrow of Odysseus.

The north wind drove them out to sea, where they ranged the wild ocean for three days, living on half a handful of maize a day. At the Mississippi Delta Pánfilo Narváez and two others, in a boat without food or water and no anchor except a stone, were blown out to sea and never heard of again. By sunset of the fourth day the others with Cabeza de Vaca were near death and lay crumpled upon one another in the barge. At evening they sighted the shore, and crawled from the boat on their hands and knees. There was rainwater in a ravine, where they made a fire, parching some of the maize. Then the boat sank, drowning three of them. The

Indians, viewing the groveling heap of dying men, were so smitten with sorrow for them that they sat on the ground and howled for their misery like animals in the wilderness.

The Spaniards named the island Malhado, meaning misfortune. The Castilians called coves, straits, and great brute waters by the softest names to woo the Virgin Mary or Saint James or the elements. On the border between Guatemala and Honduras one of the cruelest rapids is Gracias a Dios.

Worse than the forests and the seas was hunger. When their companions perished, the living dried and preserved the cadavers, and cut them into collops for food. The Indians on the island, who gathered up the dust of their dead and drank it with water as a funeral rite, regarded the Spaniards who ate each other with horror.

The natives of Malhado were nude, the women alone covering some parts of their person with wool they plucked from a tree. When they visited one another they remained silent half on hour, and frequently wept when they crossed the threshold of a friend. They cured the sick by blowing and breathing upon them, and demanded that the Spaniards, more dead than alive, drive out the infirmities of those that were ill. When Cabeza de Vaca and his companions said they had no experience in such arts, they refused to give them any food. The Spaniards were in a sore perplexity; either they had to touch the blind, the infected, and the hurt, or they must perish.

Of the many sorrows of men none is more piercing than the cry of the red savages on the Isle of Doom. "Touch me that I may be healed!" Not Solomon's chant of fatigue, nor Job's desolation on the muckheap is so great a burden for man to bear as isolation. Concord lies on a swamp, and the Puritans, building it in the wilderness, suffered more from the strokes of loneliness than they did from the bog and the briars. The pilgrims at Plymouth Plantation were stricken by spasms of desolation though they were together.

Solitude is the frontier's sign of Cain; Cain was sent into the woods of Nod for his fratricidal sin. The nomadic habit had become so dominant among the red peoples that children often deserted their parents to wander in thickets, having no other food but palm cabbage, berries, and roots. The Greeks and Romans looked upon barbarians as banished men who had been driven into the forests. Here was the stigma of the dispersion. Hordes, deriving from countless nations, from Abraham and Magog, or Scythia, from Cush or Ethiopia, from Ham or Africa, and from Mizraim or Egypt, were to make their epitaphs in America. These were the ruins of Asia, and the small wreck of Europeans who had fallen into a spurious infancy. These people living savage, aged slowly; the wrinkles of Tiresias or of Nestor came late to the Indian because his faculty is sluggish from long disuse.

After the men left the Isle of Doom, they went naked and cast their skins twice a year like serpents. Cabeza de Vaca peddled pine cones, stones, the sea snail, and conch in exchange for deerskin, maize, beans, canes, and the ocher with which the Indians rubbed their faces. Sometime in April de Vaca and his companions went down the coast, going barefoot among the marshes and the creeks which flow into the Gulf, subsisting on crabs and rockweed. They were in the land of indigence.

On their way toward the Colorado River, they encountered Indians, mostly blind, like the Bosphorus Cimmerians in the *Odyssey*. The neighbors of these eyeless savages were the Yguazes, who threw their female children to dogs so that their enemies could not marry them and become powerful. When an Yguazes had a bad dream, he destroyed his male child. These people bought a common wife for a bow, but a very good one for two arrows. They held marriage of little account, and had connection with women whenever they desired. These natives lived on roots, which gave them fierce pangs in their intestines, and they ate lizards, salamanders, ants, earth, wood, and deer dung. The women spent the nights baking roots in the ovens, while the men drank a liquor made from the mescal button, which brought about ecstatic torpor. Despite the stepmother ground, which starved them most of the year, and contrary to all laws of nature, the Yguazes were a jocular people and rioted during the prickly-pear season. They were a Texas tribe as ferocious as the Teyas, after whom that state takes its name. These savages had slain three of the Christians for going from one hovel to another. By now the Narváez expedition had dwindled to four men, Cabeza de Vaca, Castillo Maldonado, Andrés Dorantes, and Estevanico the blackamoor.

The wandering healers had a retinue of three to four thousand Indians. Out of the Indians' larder of dearth they provided spiders and worms, having nothing for their own children who were suckled until they were twelve because there was hardly any other nourishment for them. Hunger and want made the Indian and the horse restless and nomadic; the North American Indian tied a board around his abdomen when he had no food; hunger is a god of few legends. Poverty, when shared, is a wound that can be cured by a calabash of water or a tea brewed of oak leaves. The palsied and the cold wanted to put their hands on de Vaca's arm, breast, or foot. In the eight years of wandering he seldom wore a garment, and when he returned to Mexico City and the Viceroy gave him clothes, he could not endure them nor sleep anywhere except on the ground.

These savages begged Cabeza de Vaca to dissolve a stupor, a pain in the head or entrails; one was said to be dead, for the natives threw down his hut—which meant the sun no longer knew him—but when Cabeza de Vaca touched him, he arose and walked. The sick announced that they were sound when he blew upon their hurts. Among the Maya of Yucatán the ashes of a red parrot's feathers were regarded as a cure for yellow fever. But what nostrum is there for the castaways in the earth save the loving hand? Is there a medicine for the outcast, more dead than stones, who know not when the fish spawn nor how to garner the resin out of the trees? What can be done for these strangers who wean themselves from sunrise?

The western people have sepulchered away the sun and the moon; and the American is far from the Indian rivers, bays, rain, and maize that give him images, without which he is sourceless. Until he is connected with the fens, the ravines, the stars, he is more solitary than any beast. Man is a god, and kin to men, when he is a river, a mountain, a horse, a moon.

For seventeen days, in the plains between the ranges of the Sierra Madre, de Vaca and his companions' fare was a handful of deer suet each day. Then they found the Opata tribes of Sonora, who ate nothing for a third part of the year but powdered rush and straw. At one settlement, on the Rio Sonora, the three white healers, and the Berber, Estevanico, received six hundred hearts of deer in gratitude for touching the natives!

Cabeza de Vaca's pilgrimage is a wild fable of nakedness and love; it is the primitive American scripture of pioneer men in exile together. When Cristóbal Colón arrived, there was no livestock in the new hemisphere. On his second voyage he carried with him five brood mares and twenty stallions. De Soto brought thirteen pigs to Florida. Coronado, marching through Kansas, found the wild progeny of De Soto's sows. It is told that Pedro Mendoza turned five mares and seven horses loose in Buenos Aires some time after 1535 and that their issue ran mad in great droves over the pampas; by 1600 the Patagonians were horsemen. Cabeza de Vaca and Coronado after him had seen the bison, which they called the woolly cow. Mnevis and Serapis were the sacred bulls of Osiris; when Poseidon lay with Ceres, she conceived a horse. Hindu writing is meditative, and the domestic heifer is sacred and near the Buddha. The American legend is the mesa and the bison; it is the myth of a tragic terrain stalked by banished men.

EARTH, said to be somewhere in the Sea of Darkness, was known as Antilia, or Antilles, the name later given to the West Indies. De Soto, sacking Golconda, had been unable to persuade Cabeza de Vaca to join him. The Opatas of Sonora had told Estevanico of the seven emerald pueblos in New Mexico. Sesame is yellow, which is one of the colors in Paradise. The carbuncle burns in Eden, and the emerald is as green as the leek. Pliny thought Elysium was an empurpled island.

Antonio de Mendoza, Viceroy of Mexico, dispatched Fray Marcos and Estevanico to Cíbola. The friar, old and in poor health, sent the blackamoor, eager for fame, ahead while he dawdled, ate, and gathered more Cíbola apocrypha. Indian couriers arrived every few days with astounding tidings from Estevanico which nourished the sleepy ears of the monk. The friar had never been tutored by the Gospels of Quetzalcoatl, the god who taught the Aztecs to pierce the sinning tongue. Estevanico, accoutered with rattles, feathers, and turquoise, carrying a shaman's gourd and surrounded by a large covey of concubines, arrived in Cíbola. He was killed almost immediately. Some say that the Zuñis were hostile to the alien gourd supposed to have curative properties, others relate that Estevanico's retinue of paramours aroused ill feeling. The reason for his death is as obscure as the Fray Marcos *Relación*, which Cortés said was spurious.

The sick monk claimed to have made the pilgrimage from Compostela to the New Mexico settlements on foot in far less time than it took the mounted Spanish in Coronado's expedition. Coronado took a large herd of sheep, whose hooves were worn to the quick after one-third of the journey over the foothills and mesa to Cíbola. The Fray Marcos *Relación* is *tabula rasa* geography, without even the specters of rivers and mountain ranges or the odor and stigma of the *despoblado*, the starved, untilled plains and forest tracts the monk mentions.

Baltasar de Gallegos, the castellan of de Soto, had sold his houses, vineyards, a rent of wheat, and the olive fields in Seville, to seek Jason's fortune. Cortés had made a journey to lower California, in quest of Cíbola. When the friar returned to Mexico City, giving such bloated reports of the vast riches of the southwest Indians, the Viceroy selected a gentleman from Salamanca, Francisco Vásquez de Coronado, to lead an army to that realm.

In 1540 Coronado started his march at Compostela, accompanied by three hundred Spaniards, eight hundred natives, a pair of friars, including Marcos, and plump horses. The army, passing through morose and pelting towns, Chiametla, Culiacán, was particularly dispirited when reaching Chichilticalli, noised to be a famous city but which consisted of a roofless house built of red earth. The Red House, which is what it means in Aztec, marked the beginning of the wild, peopleless regions.

The men went farther into the rough Sierras, where they saw mountain goats galloping in flocks of more than one hundred each. Instead of the palm wine of Babylon, the Spaniards drank the milk of the serpent cactus fruit, which gave them violent fevers. After fifteen days in the forests, the Spaniards reached the Zuñi River, and shortly after that they came to a drab village, containing a small assortment of houses three or four stories high, which was Cíbola. The soldiers wanted to kill the monk Marcos, who was hurried back to Mexico City by Coronado. The pueblo, now in ruins, was Hawikuh, the first of the seven legendary cities. Cíbola, like Quetzalcoatl, the issue of dust and rain, was no god or Chichen Itza.

After a skirmish with the Indians, Coronado took possession of the little adobe town of terraced houses with no streets. Coronado then sent out a party to find his ships lost in the Gulf of California. They came upon nude giants who appeared to be as tall as the Patagonians whom Magellan had encountered. These giants lived in underground huts of straw, baked their loaves in ashes, and were men of immense strength, loading on their heads a fardel of three to

217

four hundred pounds. They went naked despite the great cold, and carried a firebrand to keep themselves warm. The Spaniards, desiring to build barges of reed, asked the giants to help them, and they were most obliging, as they hoped to catch the soldiers on the water and drown them. After a battle with these human towers of Sonora, the men returned to the army.

Coronado remained at Cíbola, while one group of about twenty soldiers went to the Grand Canyon. It is parched land of twisted scrub pines, and well-nigh waterless. The Indian women carried gourds of water, which were buried in the ground along the route so that on the return none would sicken of thirst.

Other Spaniards found the village Acoma atop a rocky mesa. The Indians rubbed the sweat of the horses on themselves to show that they desired peace. When one of these earthen men wished to express his sorrow for a misdeed, he wept, meaning that he intended to be docile. The natives at Acoma brought the Spaniards maize loaves, piñon nuts, cornmeal, and tanned deerskins, and led them into the town playing drums and flutes.

It snowed ten days, covering the junipers and pines. When the army encamped, the horses stood half-buried in it. The snow was so dry that it lay over the soldiers sleeping on the ground as a warm blanket. A dead turkey cock will not molder or give off a bad smell for sixty days because the air is so dry in this country, and the same is true of a dead man. The sky of Quito, the ancient Inca city, has a similar piercing purity that makes men walk the earth as though they contained the cosmos.

The Spaniards arrived next at Tiguex. The pueblos in

this region have no streets, and as the houses are without doors, the only access to the village was up a ladder to the roof. The natives, like the pre-Christian Essenes, excreted at a distance from the settlement. Thy had kivas, which are underground religious chambers, and a corn room containing a trough with three stones: one the women broke the corn with, the other was to grind it, and the third to grind it again.

Tiguex, as well as the pueblos of Cíbola, had an estufa, which is a hot talk room where men gathered together for counsel. There is a great deal of sense to this, as cold conversation brings men tombs, mischief, and wars, instead of friendship. The women cover themselves entirely, and are shown the most tender regard. When a man wishes to marry, he weaves a blanket, placing it before the woman he desires to be his bride, and like Ruth sleeping at the foot of Boaz on the granary floor, she covers herself with it and becomes his wife.

A Spaniard at Tiguex, observing a pretty Indian woman, asked her husband to hold his horse while he pretended to go to the village but instead ravished the wife. The Indians took their vengeance by driving the horses toward the pueblo, shooting arrows at them, and killing many, including seven of Coronado's mules. The Indian nations of the Americas looked upon the horse as a divine brute. After Cortés had left a lame horse in Guatemala, the Maya brought him fowl, meat, and flowers, which killed the animal.

After the Indian woman was violated, a fifty-day battle followed. The natives then surrendered because their water failed. There is so little rainfall in this country that the inhabitants at Tiguex made the mortar for the adobe bricks with human urine. The Iberians, forefathers of the Spanish, scrubbed their teeth with urine according to Catullus and Diodorus.

The Indians had no guileful marriage practices. The converted Aztecs came to the church to be married followed by so many mistresses that the priests sometimes joined the wrong man and woman to each other. When the Aztec was asked to give up his concubines, he said the Spaniards had many women too. The monks replied that these were the servants of the Christians, to which the Indians answered, "The women we keep are our servants also."

The nomadic, coastal Indians cohabited with women at random. The damsels of one tribe were regarded as communal prostitutes until they were wives. In the province of Culiacán, where Coronado's soldiers were for several days, the women who wished to remain unmarried were given subtle clothes and turquoise and placed in a house, and anybody who wanted to go in and lie with one of them could, so that she was not wasted. Men bought their wives on market days. After she was purchased, the chief cohabited with her first, and if he could not deflower her, the price was returned to the man.

At Petatlán, in the province of Culiacán, the women dressed in petticoats of tanned deerskin; in one of the islands in the South Seas the women wore a shift made of the rind of a tree; at Massana, which Magellan visited, the girls were very pretty, adorned only with a small girdle of palm-tree cloth. In Cicuye, the largest pueblo in New Mexico, the virgins, despite the severe weather, went naked until they took husbands. The Aztecs were lascivious but buried their spouses with the spindle and distaff, indicating their respect for feminine virtue. The Quiché Maya held that the flesh of woman was first made of rushes, which can be woven into a basket for fruit or a maiden. After the siege of Tiguex had ended, one band of soldiers went to look for the Gulf of Mexico. The army under Coronado was ordered to start for Quivira, another legendary Patagonia. On the route they came to a settlement of Querechos, the old name of the eastern Apaches, who lived in tents of bison skins. The Querechos did not sow maize, or eat bread, but lived on raw meat and fruit; they opened the belly of the bison, squeezed out the sodden grass, and drank the juice that was left. They carried the gut of a buffalo filled with blood around their necks to slake their thirst when traveling through the deserts. The Querechos waited till the sun rose and then shot an arrow in the direction they desired to go.

Coronado's soldiers had to drop the bones and dung of the bison on the prairie to make a trail for lost game hunters. Right after prairie grass is trampled upon it waxes stiff. One thousand horses, five hundred bison, five thousand rams and ewes, Coronado's army, and fifteen hundred Indians passed over the mesa grass without leaving a record of one foot or a hoof.

The men reached Quivira, which lay in Nebraska and Kansas. Instead of the one-and-a-half-foot ruby of the great Khan of Cathay, they found plums, grapes, nuts, and flax. The journey was a wretched failure, and Coronado was in disgrace with the Viceroy at Mexico City. The soldiers had known invincible sufferings, and going back to Culiacán and Compostela, half-naked and lice-ridden, they had the satisfaction of the hopeless solely gratified by the prodigies of the New World. Numerous men had been sorely wounded by the poisoned arrows of a fierce, hilly tribe, and all died when struck until they were told by a native to drink the juice of wild quince.

XI

DE SOTO HAD ACHIEVED an odyssey though his deeds were ferine; his darkest acts were healed by the strength with which he committed them. He found the Mississippi River, but he lost an India in pearls because he was amorous.

The vessels in de Soto's armada bore the names of saints, and the appellations of the inlets and coves are the homage they paid to their misfortunes. The Bay of the Holy Spirit and the River of Discords are the sighs of these geographers. They wanted to own *Tierra Nueva*, and for their evil desires the place was translated into a nemesis instead of an angel, and most of them perished or were deprived of their wits.

The discoverers came to rob the ground and streams of

their minerals. Locality was a god to the Indian caciques, who had the names of the rivers, the hills, or the forests where they abode. There was hostility between one Indian settlement and another, and the victors decapitated their enemies, enslaved their wives and children, but seldom took the land.

De Soto, a most civil Iago, gave the Indian *curaca*, or lord, silks, mirrors, and shirts, and embraced him with the greatest affection. He commanded his cavalry to ride as a martial battalion, and the natives thought the horse and man were a single beast. The *curaca* bowed low, kissing the hands of the *adelantado* de Soto, and his Indians came with maize, grapes, dried prunes, fish, and marten furs, while the warriors hid in the forests or near lagoons, their bows and arrows covered by grass.

The Floridians were tall, more than two yards in length, and the Inca Garcilaso de la Vega related that the giant Tascaluza had a waistline that was more than two-thirds of a metre. The men had handsome, brutal countenances, and wore just enough chamois cloth to conceal their haunches and secret parts. The women covered their whole bodies with chamois. Their bows, made of oak, were as hard to draw as the one which Odysseus alone had the strength to use against the suitors of Penelope.

The littoral regions were marshland, and the tumid rivers rose as high as sixty leagues. The maritime soil was so barren that there were times when the Spaniards lived on sea snails and booby birds. The Spanish soldiers in Yucatán and Guatemala ate the inside of the *kunché* bark, which is mellow and soft.

Acorn was his forest milk, of chestnuts he kneaded wild bread, athirst he died mad in the salt estuaries, and hungry, no frigate bird pecked more damage; his burial site was the trunk of a tree or a swamp. Mountain roots, amaranth, unsown rye purge the eye, hyssop and gall and ravine strengthen the knees: He was a Hercules whose works were evil.

Before Hernando de Soto had proclaimed the Kingdom of Florida a possession of Emperor Charles the Fifth, the Cacique Hirrihigua seized four Spaniards who had come to this province with Pánfilo de Narváez. He took them to the plaza of the village, commanding them to run while the Indians shot arrows at them. This gave him such pleasure that he ordered his warriors to torture Juan Ortiz, an eighteen-year-old "fledgling cavalier," but his wife and three daughters beseeched the cacique to spare him, and because of their tender entreaties, he interrupted this spectacle.

Hirrihigua had received some injustices from the Spaniards, who had thrown his mother to the dogs to be eaten; when the cacique had occasion to blow his nose, he could not find it. De Soto had cut off the lips and chins of Indians and severed the heads of fainting couriers rather than trouble to untie the iron collars to which they were yoked. De Soto's Spaniards had seized an Indian guide to lead them back to the bay. After marching in a circle through woods and bogs, eating roots and grass for many days, and discovering that they had been deceived, they threatened to give the Indian to the mastiffs if he did not take them back to the sea, which was only several leagues away. He promised to obey them, and circling the forests again and making the Spaniards endure more terrible suffering, he was thrown to the dogs, who devoured him.

Hernando de Soto took the greatest pains to gain kind deeds of the cacique Vitachuco, who had sent many

225

messengers to him, promising that he would command the ground and hills to swallow the Spaniards; he had also ordered the birds to drop a venom on the conquistadors which would cause them to rot. However, the *adelantado* invited Vitachuco to his camp; and after the exchange of many courtesies and vows of friendship, de Soto's men entered the cacique's deserted village. The Indians hidden in the woods discharged their arrows at the Spaniards the entire day; others remained in a cold lagoon where the water was so deep that, while three or four Indians swam, one stood on their backs so that he could shoot his arrows at the enemy. When the Indians, numb with the waters of the lagoon, refused to surrender, they were seized by Spaniards who swam after them and dragged them ashore, after which the Governor gave them mirrors and silks and sent them home. De Soto then invited the cacique to his table, and Vitachuco, who had an enormous, violent body, rose while his host was still eating and, seizing the *adelantado* by the neck, gave him a blow over the eyes, the mouth, and the nose. Then falling upon his prone and half-dead victim, he began to mangle de Soto until the Spaniards killed the savage.

Traveling for days with no food except grass and the tendrils of vines, the miserable band and their captain came to Cofachiqui. After receiving them, the princess of that realm removed a long necklace, the pearls of which were as large as hazelnuts, and gave it to de Soto. She then took them to her ancestral graveyard, where the dead were deposited in baskets woven out of cane. There were twenty-five thousand pounds of pearls in this charnel house, which were held of little worth by the Spaniards because they had been pierced by copper needles and the smoke had somewhat discolored them. Hernando do Soto had instructed his soldiers to make rosaries of the pearls, but all the pearls were lost or cast away.

The lady of Cofachiqui, a beauty with immense modesties, was asked to accompany the *adelantado*. The Inca said these brutish Dianas were very chaste, but when a Spaniard was caught by several Indian women, they gave him agonies by pounding his genital organs, and he either perished or suffered from another horrible affliction. On one of their marches the maiden Cofachiqui went into a thicket to relieve herself, and carrying a chest of pearls, escaped with a Moor from Barbary and two negro slaves.

After de Soto had perished in the wilderness, the Spanish remnant, of no more than three hundred, departed in boats that were miserable river huts and were pursued by Indians in canoes for a thousand miles down the Mississippi.

The European succumbed to the new continent; it was sterile earth which brewed fatal ends. Indian earth was a negative Golgotha. Martin Carvalho, a Portugal, went with over two hundred men in quest of gold, which is almost as indestructible as avarice. They came upon a crystal mountain and then saw a river between two mountains which shone like the stones of Ophir. They bit the grains with their teeth to determine whether it was a precious metal. In desert country their sustenance was some grass; one day they caught a snake upon which they supped. Sick and fearful of the red savages, they turned back in canoes, going on the River Cricare; in a rapid the canoe containing the gold was lost. After eight months of starvation, they returned to Porto Seguro utterly poor, their hopes dead.

The Spanish hidalgo and adventurer came for riches, but the loot was often no more than the piñon nut, tanned hides of the woolly cattle of the Platte, or virgin discovery, which, like learning, is tombstone destiny.

Beneath the crust of the Christian was the new earth and riparian heathen. The discoverers found wild ground that slaked their own natures. One ransacking customs to understand man is no less baffled than Montezuma was when, seeing Cortés and his soldiers kneeling to the Rood, he asked why they humbled themselves before an ordinary tree.

XII

Ginger, cassia, storax paint the Moluccas in the blood.
Magellan's men are glyphic bones at the Popinjays, the
ague breathes prayer into the visage as dotish as the penguin
in the Straits, pepper draws mirth from the Pole Antarctic.
Potosi, under the tropics, is desert rock, cold and grassless.

Magellan watered at the Isle of Thieves, lost rope, tackle,
a Portugal shirt, hawk's bells, he guerdoned the natives with
arrows they plucked as holy relics from the flesh, and, dying,
marveled how heaven drank their olive blood.

Men are milder on their knees, though ever chaffering with
doom shackled to chance. Gathering wrack in the windy

229

Magellans, the sole lodestar of sea-worn hearts was their daughters at Cádiz, and remembering these immaculate maids of their Andalusia, *entered a wild tract of water, named it the Strait of the Eleven Thousand Virgins.*

Man is just and energetic in battle, but at home sensual, a perjurer, and a malicious neighbor. The ten thousand Greeks were querulous and venal until they saw one of their men, betrayed by the Persian Tissaphernes, carrying the Greek's intestines in his hands.

Cyrus the younger had an ecstatic nature and could not taste the best of wine or of breads without sending partly emptied flagons of it or half-eaten loaves to his friends. Cyrus was a military seer; he so abhorred chicane, deceit, sloth, and injustice that any number of his soldiers were without hands, legs, and eyes. How can one account for the human mind? The Euphrates is one of the rivers in Paradise, but the Arabian plains along its banks are covered with wormwood.

At Hochelaga Jacques Cartier saw a savage with some pelts around his body which looked like the papyri that grow in the Nile but which were the skins of a foe. In northwest America the natives came to the ships of Captain Cook with the skulls and the hands of enemies which they sought to barter for iron and nails.

One cacique told Cartier of a region, a moon's journey from Hochelaga, laden with oranges and almonds, which are the fruits of desire that killeth the will. The Indians sowed miracles no less than Mandeville, and they mentioned a people born with one leg who voided nothing but water. But this was less of a prodigy than the throng of Indians, some senile, and others crippled or with diseased eyes, who came to be healed simply by touching Cartier.

Indian savages showed their love by stroking the breast of a stranger. When Cartier had looked for a place to disembark but could not, a barbarian swam to the vessel and, carrying Cartier to land, embraced him. At one of the islands in the South Seas, a dying soldier begged Magellan to give him a plaister of the intestines of a native for his fever. Wounded Spaniards took the fat of a slain Indian to assuage their own wounds.

The bowels of our foes cure us no less than those of our friends, for men, if peace is their yoke and boredom, can only clasp one another's hands when they are struggling together against their adversaries; for men apart are criminals and only together are sane.

The ground was vindictive; the savin, laurel, the alligator tree madden the faculties. At Canada the soldiers of Jacques Cartier were dying of a *Nueva Firma* plague; the teeth were cast out, the mouth fell away, and they had the stench of holy Lazarus in his grave. Opening the body of a youth just dead of the scurvy, they found the heart, which looked like milky quartz, and the water about it was the color of the jubilant Babylonian date. The dying French lay in the snows behind the palisades, fearing that the Indians would massacre all of them.

Cartier, meeting a savage, cured of the scurvy, furtively enquired how he had recovered. Without guile the Indian said he had cooked the bough of a spruce with its leaves and drunk the decoction every third day.

Ragged earth seldom produces mild men; the rivers of the New Continent are choleric, and the reason that the rapacious Scamander, with whom Achilles fought, appears to be small and of little importance is that Homer has tamed this stream.

The Viceroy Don de Luna y Arellano with an army of fifteen hundred soldiers set out to conquer the kingdom of Florida. After anchoring in a fine, halcyon bay, a hurricane broke the ships to pieces. A thousand survivors had no food until they came to a settlement called Nanipacna, where the corn was so harsh they had to soak it in sea water and then in fresh water to make it palatable. As there were not enough leaves, twigs, and bark for victuals, the men chewed the rawhide linings of their bucklers just as Aeneas and his companions kept themselves alive by gnawing their wooden trenchers. Summer chestnuts and the walnut tree sustained them for a fifty days' march to Olibahali, where they bartered beads and some cloth for vegetables, fruit, and corn.

The Spaniards found an aromatic to relieve them of pains, and they made a rosary of these herbs, which they carried around their necks. A Frenchman had discovered American sassafras, that has the odor of fennel, in which Prometheus hid the fire he had stolen from Zeus. Sassafras grows by the sea, and causes stones to pass, and was reckoned good for the pox. Perhaps, it is too marvelous an agony to suffer simply to discover fennel, sassafras, or to pursue the river tracks of the Cephisus to its source. Homer has no disdain, and the least he knows is poetry. Demeter ranged the whole earth in search of her daughter, Persephone, who plants hyacinth, violets, lupines, as she wanders.

Insolent Pelias paid for Jason's expedition to the River Phasis in Colchis. Menelaus, Ulysses, Jason, were the freebooters of the seas; Drake, Magellan, the Norse, were briny robbers. Martin Frobisher, covetous of ivory, electrum, and silver as Menelaus, came over the North Sea looking for the strait to China. He loaded his ship with the

Colchian precious metals, and when he returned, he found that he had a cargo of gravel. Frobisher had discovered estuaries, bays, isles, a channel that bears his name, and gravel, which is not all dross.

English voyagers had come to Nova Zembla, discovered by William Barents; their diet was deer, sea cows, bears, and the frozen seas. After eating bear's liver for a winter, all their hair fell out. Munck and his sailors had reached Nova Zembla, which is Russian for "New Land." Arctic hunger ruined their mouths and teeth; they dug up some kind of raspberry out of the ice and postponed dying. In the month of May geese, swans, little hoopoes, woodcocks, swallows, and falcons appeared, but they were too feeble to hunt them. Of Munck's crew of sixty-four sailors, two lived.

A Danish pilot happened upon a river of gold in Nova Zembla, and taking his cargo back to his homeland, there learned that he had carried a ship of sand across the Barents Sea. Tragedy is not so extreme a travail as folly; he died shortly afterward because, alive, he was ridiculous.

Majuelas was wrecked in Ascension Bay; the desolate shingle provided him snails and shellfish. At night he roosted in a tree and watched a tiger feeding upon a deer, and by dawn he ate what the tiger had left. At Cape Cotoch in Yucatán there was an edifice in the sea showing an idol whose flanks were being devoured by two ferocious animals; there was also a thick stone serpent that was swallowing a lion. Aguilar and his companions were cast on the coast of Yucatán; five of his men were sacrificed to the starved idols and others enslaved; all except two died grieving.

There were many martyrs of Canada and Florida, and the streams and towns that bear their names seem as apocryphal as the numerous towns of Jason that are everywhere in Armenia and in Media. The sea brigands who drowned in the Florida tides or in the Iroquois wilderness are as renowned as Juba, Ptolemy, and Aristotle; they were no worse than Jason, who was said by some to have gone far up the Ister, or even into the Exterior Sea. The Argonautic expedition was no less real than the fleets of Cristóbal Colón or Sir Walter Raleigh's quest for El Dorado in Guiana.

Freebooters like Jason who learned navigation from Aeolus came to America for the Golden Fleece, but most of them died mad or drowned in storms off the Bahamas. Magellan, bringing the Christian cross to the Moluccas, was a lunatic pirate; Frobisher was as greedy as Cacus, whom Hercules subdued. The Danes, reaching Greenland, found nothing but natives clothed in the skins of penguins and pelicans.

The friars murdered in the wilderness by an Iroquois hatchet were madmen; they kissed the stakes at which they were burnt; the Indians chewed the fingers of Father Jean Brebeuf until they were stumps, pulled out his lips and tongue, but he died without murmuring against his fate. Father Goupil died when the Indians hurled a tunic of hot chains on his naked body. Father Isaac Jogues, searching for the corpse of Goupil, found it had been eaten by dogs. Jogues returned to France, but he had such a wild zeal to bring the monstrance and the creed to the Iroquois that he came back to the Indian country, where one of these woodland brutes broke his skull with a hatchet. The diabolical Iroquois drank the blood of the monk Brebeuf to make them as brave as he. Each new century begets its perdition and mentor, and new ground, scarce weaned from Ocean, nursed the Iroquois. The annals of the race are writ in gore, a copious draught of which is titled erudition.

Fray Juan Ferrer and Padre Marcos de Mena walked naked on the shore of the Rio de los Palmas, in which two whales took their summer sleep. When the Indians returned with new arrows, they shot one into the back of Fray Juan, which killed him. The monk Marcos received seven wounds, and one of them was in his throat. He found his Spanish companions, but they were too feeble to carry him, and they buried him in the sand at the edge of the river, leaving his face uncovered so that he could breathe until he expired. Before the Spanish soldiers had reached the Panuco River, every one was slain by the Indians. The monk slept on the banks of the Tanipa, and when he awakened, the maggots were singing in his wounds. He had fallen into such a delirium that, when two Indians wrapped him in cotton blankets and carried him in a canoe to a Spanish town, he thought they were the angels whom Abraham saw beneath the terebinth at Mamre.

The friars who settled near the Canada River were Prometheans, and their malady was their desire to do good. The visionary attempts to shake the beast out of him; virtue sickens men. Those who endeavor to be just, not to lie, murder, or dupe others, are beside themselves, and they can find no friends in such a cause to be their companions. That Socrates was ill when he took the hemlock there can be no doubt; for he, like his pupil Plato, spent most of his days by the waters of Phlegethon, praying to Zeus and Hera and Hermes for death, for alive man is a liar, lecher, and thief, or else he shakes by the rivers of death.

Peter had scarce the courage to walk on water. One of the prophetic Isaiahs was said to have been sawed to pieces in the days of Manasseh, but this is an unbearable burden for the mind and drives the ghosts of all races to the furies. Seers, when they lived, were eremetic specters, who walked beside themselves, for men in this fell world are too cunning and wanton to keep them company.

Man is the animal who thinks, but he cannot employ his intellect without losing his reason, which is why Cristóbal Colón saw mermaids in the waters near the Antilles, or how Plato conceived the *Timaeus*. It would be doleful to imagine that the Golden Fleece were nothing else but the precious metals of Colchis or that Cortés, de Soto, Drake, Cook, Magellan, Cabot, seeking the strait to the khans of Tartary for nutmegs, gold, and emeralds, were not water-philosophers.

The Patagonians, living wretched, as though this were man's polestar, are gigantic boys and girls. The lives of the Chippeways, the Patagonians, the Fuegians, the Guaraunos are chronicles of lamentation, for all were once the sons of Apollo.

The footpath over the swift waters of the Apurimac was of osier; Daedalus could not have built the temples at Palenque or at Cuzco; the stones for the fanes and oratories at Cholula are said to have been seamed together without iron by the Toltecs or demigods. Papyrus was gathered in the Delta marshes, or by the waters at Byblos, and yet at the time of Martial and Vergil, the sacred paper from the Syrian seas or found at the Pelusiac mouth of the Nile was scarce, but abundant at Tabasco, Tenochtitlán and Mayapán. Montezuma, surrounded by concubines and enough gnomes and copal-smelling humpbacks to delight Domitian, craved gold, silver, and salves, and especially papyrus.

The Indians have many gentle traits; in Brazil the natives

devour their sick kindred because they have not so cruel a heart as to bury them and give them to a grub. There is no people more civil or timorous as those at Otaheite. When a father or mother died, the children beat their teeth with stones and thrust a shark's tooth into their heads until the blood poured upon them. They are a mild, pacific people and have no faults save thievery, which they do without skulking, and cannibalism. They have a humble deity by the name of Eatooa, whom they trundle in a handbarrow. They are very pious, given to abundant but not grum prayers, and after they have plucked out the two eyes of the corpse slain to appease Eatooa, they wrap each eye in a green leaf.

The gods that enslave men the least are those that cannot be seen, painted, or imagined. The most didactic tombs are vacant, as the crypt of Ephesian John, which contains nothing except manna.